ENJOY THE RIDE

Lessons For The Quest To Live A
Joyful, Profitable Life In Dentistry

ALAN STERN, DDS

INDIE BOOKS
INTERNATIONAL

No part of this publication may be reproduced or distributed in any form or by any means without the prior permission of the publisher. Requests for permission should be directed to permissions@indiebooksintl.com, or mailed to Permissions, Indie Books International, 2424 Vista Way, Suite 316, Oceanside, CA 92054.

The views and opinions in this book are those of the author at the time of writing this book, and do not reflect the opinions of Indie Books International or its editors.

When just a first name is used in this book, the story is true but the name has been changed to protect privacy.

Neither the publisher nor the author is engaged in rendering legal, tax, or other professional services through this book. The information is for business education purposes only. If expert assistance is required, the services of appropriate professionals should be sought. The publisher and the author shall have neither liability nor responsibility to any person or entity with respect to any loss or damage caused directly or indirectly by the information in this publication.

ISBN: 978-1-947480-90-2
Library of Congress Control Number: 2019919278

Designed by Joni McPherson, mcphersongraphics.com

Author cover photo by Devin Peppler, www.pepplerphoto.com

INDIE BOOKS INTERNATIONAL, LLC
2424 VISTA WAY, SUITE 316
OCEANSIDE, CA 92054
www.indiebooksintl.com

Dedication

To my beautiful wife, Fran, who has stood by and put up with me almost from the moment we met, risked her life to give us our two children, and strengthened and loved all of us. We are in our fifth decade of marriage. I am lucky; she is crazy.

To my children, Neil and Tracey, our two medical miracles whose lives of love, resilience, strength of character, and amazing abilities would make any parent smile ear-to-ear with a not-dry eye.

And to my mother, Magdalena Stern, 1925–2012, who endured unimaginable horror and rose from the ashes of the Holocaust to bring my brother and me into this world, and who continues to inspire and teach me long after her physical presence disappeared. I dedicate the work I will do for the rest of my life to the hope that something good will come out of the suffering she endured.

Contents

Foreword

When Dr. Alan Stern, my great friend, asked me to write a foreword for this book, I was honored and terrified. But the more I thought about it, the less scary and daunting it became. I can honestly say that Alan was, is, and will continue to be one of my best friends, although we don't see one another often enough. He's that rare individual, regardless of how long it's been since our last time together, it's as if we had talked the day before.

In that same way, it seems just like yesterday when I arrived at the Medical College of Virginia (MCV), now called Virginia Commonwealth University's School of Dentistry (VCU), at the end of summer, 1977. I remember being excited and a bit scared being in a new and very different environment having graduated from the University of Virginia that spring. Looking forward to the start of dental school, the end of a long and enjoyable educational journey, I was anxious to meet those 120 dental students that would be sharing the experience.

At MCV, students are arranged alphabetically by last name, mine being Shelburne, I was assigned a lab desk with classmates with last names close in the alphabet. Being from the south and attending schools in the south, I had very little experience with other classmates, or anybody really, from the north; and not with someone from the New York Jewish community, a "practicing" Jew from "the city." I had nothing against diverse individuals, nothing at all, but I did have preconceived notions about folks from that part of the country and background.

So, when Alan Stern (the "S" put him squarely in the close circle of students in my lab) walked into the lab with a loud laugh and a kind of in-your-face demeanor, I thought my preconceived notions were spot on. I don't know that I have ever been more wrong about a person, especially my first impression of someone, in my life. Certainly, we came from very different backgrounds with very many cultural and experiential differences.

I learned, through getting to know Alan those four years we were bound together as dental students at MCV, that we were very much more alike than we were different. Alan did and still does have one of the biggest hearts of anybody I have ever seen. He's empathetic, generous, inquisitive, funny (but not quite as funny as he thinks he is), witty, curious, but more than anything else, loving. It is *so apparent* that he loves his wife, Fran, deeply and completely, and his two children more than his own life. He loves his community, his profession, and his patients and has an endless affinity to give back what he can, when he can, to whomever he can.

Alan did not have it very easy in dental school. Although he has a brilliant mind, he did not grow up working with his hands or dealing with mechanical challenges, so some of the dental techniques we had to master were challenging for him. I think he may have worked harder than anyone else in dental school to overcome that deficit. He did not let those challenges dampen his desire to become the best clinician possible and I believe he has succeeded.

The thing he did not have to work at was his ability to connect with and empathize with his patients and with other human beings. Alan has been a lifelong learner, devoting himself to bettering himself and his technical skills so that he is now what I would call a master of the dental craft and an example of abundance. He's never been one to accept the status quo nor one to let an opportunity to improve himself and to uplift those around him pass. I learned, getting to know Alan better during those four years at MCV, just how resilient and resourceful he was and am so proud that he's continued to improve himself and is now using those life lessons to help others overcome their challenges, learn from their mistakes, and to build on their successes.

Alan's experience, education, heart, and wit make him immensely qualified to help you, the reader, become better equipped for life and practice. He's one of my heroes. No doubt, when you read this book, he will be one of yours too.

Roy S. Shelburne, DDS

Preface

L ike all dental students and dentists, I make mistakes. With a little "help" from my upbringing and a flawed educational process, those mistakes caused me to see myself, my work, and my life as woefully inadequate. It didn't have to be that way for me, and I am so grateful that it no longer is.

I am an imperfect practitioner of an imperfect art. I am an imperfect father, husband, son, brother, and friend. I am an imperfect leader, speaker, and coach. But I have come to know myself from a better, healthier point of view, and to realize that I am pretty darned good at everything I've done.

My work makes people better. So does yours.

I am a miracle to those who know me. So are you.

And the sooner you understand that you are all this and more, life will get better. I promise.

Alan Stern
September 2019

Lesson 1

A Life In Dentistry Is Challenging

"Dental school is a launchpad for divorce."

That was the first thing I remember hearing from one of our deans at Medical College of Virginia/Virginia Commonwealth University School of Dentistry. What an incredibly demoralizing thing to say to a group of people aspiring to be healers.

But the dean was correct, to a degree. A fair number of our married classmates entering dental school in that summer of 1977 did wind up divorcing. Having been married a week and a day before hearing those words, I was scared. Forty-plus years later, I feel blessed.

The dental school was primarily interested in creating oral repair people with disregard to anything else.

So, the stress of the dental school curriculum took its toll. Perhaps the stress accelerated the inevitable on young couples who couldn't get through it "for better or for worse." Or perhaps a little bit of preparation or counseling might have helped. We'll never know.

Back in the seventies and earlier, no school saw its responsibility to anything other than academics, which was the norm for that era. But if our education blinded us to the human reality of being a student, how could we have been expected to see the human side of the people we would treat or the human side of what it's like to practice as a forever imperfect dentist and human being? The simple truth is that it couldn't. The simple truth is that the actual dentistry is merely a part of what we do; in fact, it is the end product of a long process that must begin with some level of connection.

So many things have to happen before we do that technical stuff school taught us. And it is these things which really affect our lives and enable us to powerfully affect others.

What we do is special. Rachel Remen, in her book, *My Grandfather's Blessings*, teaches that many of us live far more meaningful lives than we know. This is so true for anyone practicing dentistry. What impact does your work have on the day-to-day life of each soul you encounter? From the rehabilitation of a diseased mouth to (what we see as) a *simple* direct restoration, you have altered the quality—and sometimes the quantity—of a person's life.

Whether you provide elective or essential services, you can create sacred moments and affect someone for the better every day; and, in doing so, reinforce the very special nature of your unique brand to yourself and everyone you encounter.

Dentists Do Sacred Work

Let's start by taking a look at the human side of dentistry, which is where the real power of what you do every day resides.

First, let's look at how you can use your power for the benefit of others. Let's start with a story.

I practice in a condominium complex with nine other medical and dental offices in three separate buildings. One Christmas morning, I ran into my neighbor, Harvey (*author's note: when just first names are used in this book, the story is true but the name is changed to protect privacy*), an obstetrician-gynecologist. We greeted each other and I asked Harvey what he was doing for the holiday. He shrugged and grimaced and said that he was on call and he was going to the hospital for the next twenty-four hours. My response to him was that he was forced into a position of generosity and privilege for which so few are qualified and for which many people would be grateful.

"That's one way of looking at it, I guess," he responded.

We parted with my hope that he'd share/experience the joy of delivering Christmas babies to some very thankful parents.

I am privileged to have known a lot of school teachers. Teaching is an amazing profession and teachers occupy a critical position of influence for everyone they encounter. For example, can you remember who won an Oscar or the American League MVP the year you were in first grade? I certainly can't, but I bet you *can* remember who your first grade teacher was. School teachers are special; their ability to change lives is every bit as powerful as that of dentists. But they are accountable to bureaucracies that are stifling. They teach to test. They're evaluated not on their performance, not on their care, not on their love for children; rather, they are evaluated on students' test scores and are severely restricted in their use of judgment, something which experience brings to them.

Can you imagine being evaluated by a faceless bureaucrat for the outcomes of your work on people who eat tons of sugar and don't brush or floss their teeth? We have a fantastic profession where we are still able to exercise our five greatest talents—care, skill, judgment, leadership, and influence for the good of others. And although some practices are subject to the whim of insurance companies and other third-party payers, most, if not all, of us can practice with little or no micromanagement to cause us to burn out. We merely have to look up from that crown, filling, impression, or extraction site and see the real value of what we can do every day.

I will never forget Mildred, a lady in her upper seventies who suffered from MS and could not walk. Mildred asked me to correct her severely deformed, discolored, and mottled anterior teeth. The work was very difficult for numerous relatively unimportant reasons. Our entire team put countless hours improving her home care, preparing her soft tissues, and preparing and provisionalizing her teeth, making her as comfortable as possible in our chair.

When the time came to deliver her ceramic crowns, Mildred took one look in the mirror and asked us to bring her husband into the treatment room. "Paul," Mildred asked, "can you take me driving around town so I can just smile at people?"

There was not a dry eye in the office that day. Our hygienist, our assistant, and our front desk person (who is also my wife) all joined Mildred and Paul in the treatment room to congratulate her. How much impact do you think our crown-and-bridge had on the lady who couldn't walk, but whose self-esteem and self-efficacy were renewed by what we dentists see as just another procedure?

I had a young man come up to me recently to thank me for talking to him about stopping tobacco chewing. I may very well have saved his life with a few well-spoken and well-timed words. If that wasn't a sacred moment worth living for, I don't know what was.

How many times a day do these sacred moments occur in your life? How have you used your power as the person called *Doctor* to influence someone? Have you greeted the UPS guy, the FedEx lady, the letter carrier, or the custodian by their names and with a smile? Do you and your team even know their names? Have you complimented, educated, trained, or thanked your team? In an era where criticism flows so quickly and fiercely and when mistakes are seriously consequential, an enthusiastic and sincere acknowledgment of your team's successes is so valuable. They'll love you for it and will be motivated to continue to improve. Every one of these simple actions provides your own unique support to another person.

So, stop for a moment, look up from that composite, extraction site, and set of veneers and smell the roses of the greatness of your wonderful, albeit imperfect work.

Keep the passion that drove you to pursue a career in this great profession alive by savoring the power of your position that you use for the betterment of others every single day. Most importantly, try to begin your day (and ask your team to begin their day) by asking yourself, "Whose life/lives will I make better today?" and end the day by answering that very question.

If You're Not Excited, *Get* Excited.

Many dentists I know have become bored or burned out after doing the same thing for many years. The reality, however, is that we can learn new things and offer new services at any time in our careers. Innovations in implant prosthetics, airway management, Invisalign, and the oral-systemic connection are exciting. You don't have to keep doing the same old, same old. Get out of your comfort zone, take some good courses, latch on to something new, get excited, and project that excitement in your office.

Fall In Love Again

After forty-six years of knowing one another, my wife's and my love is as strong as ever. But our love today is very different from what it was in decades past; it has to be because neither one of us is the same as we were in our late teens and twenties when we met. The years of excitement, discovery, heavy passion, and carefree fun have given way to newer ways of loving one another and enjoying the life we've built. The same transition of love applies to our relationship with our children as they have grown from total dependency into independent, unique people with terrific careers and very nice lives of their own.

You can maintain a loving relationship with your career in dentistry in much the same way. In addition to learning new things, you can recognize the significance of your work to others. You can work to develop your team's level of skill and knowledge. You can get out into the community as a resource for wellness. Use your knowledge and experience in new and creative ways. Light a spark inside of yourself. Remember the reason that you chose dentistry as a career. Find your *why* and let dentistry help you express your special gifts to the world. Shed your fear of failure. As long as you have the best interests of another human being in mind when you work, you may fall down a few times and you may learn a few lessons the hard way, but *you will not lose.* Develop a network of like-minded general dentists and specialists. Offer your expertise to them and ask for theirs. There are at least ten dentists within walking distance of my office. I view them as colleagues and not as competitors. Some of them have come to me for guidance which I have given generously. I may even have saved the life of one dentist across the street from me with my health advice. And I have gone to them when I needed stuff. Get out of *competitor* mode, get into *colleague* mode, and watch yourself and everyone around you prosper.

Lesson 2

What Doesn't Kill You Teaches You To Be Better

he poet Khalil Gibran wrote that: "Your pain is the shell that encloses your understanding".

My pain is that I was born to a Holocaust survivor and a man who had tremendous difficulty practicing and expressing empathy.

My mother is one of my heroes. A faulted and flawed human being, scarred by the trauma unimaginable to anyone who hasn't lived through it, she battled demons daily to try to live her life and raise two children despite her horrifically negative view of life.

She was known to say that Jewish people were put on this earth to suffer. And who could blame her? She was literally torn from her parents who were sent to their deaths at Auschwitz while she labored as a slave in what should have been exciting years of growth and self-discovery. She felt the guilt of one who survived while her loved ones died and, overtly or subliminally, transmitted those feelings to all she knew.

My father was an American soldier who met my mother shortly after she was liberated from Auschwitz. He was a talented intelligence officer who was instrumental in garnering critical information for the Allied victory in World War II. He was raised as a religious man in a very traditional home by two Hungarian-Jewish immigrants. And as a product of the strict, patriarchal, *my-way-or-the-highway* early twentieth century model of family that was my grandparents' view of life, I'm not sure he had the skills to face the challenges that a husband to my very troubled mother needed so badly.

So I am the product of the world's greatest mass murder and a marriage that should never have happened under the best of circumstances. A miracle. And, by the way, my wife and I are an infertile couple. So our children, one of whom was born on my mother the Holocaust survivor's sixty-first birthday, are miracles. The miracles that are me and our children have sustained me with gratitude for most of my life. But the demons of having been caught in the crossfire of my two most critical role models and mind-shapers, along with the difficulties posed by the *my-way-or-the-highway* approach of a dominant parent, scarred me in ways that would not heal for decades. I was also bullied in grade school by classmates who saw and exploited my emotional fragility and were simply too immature to recognize it for what it was. How

I functioned socially, academically, and free of substance abuse outside of normal college drinking shenanigans is astonishing; another miracle cast upon my life. Beneath it all, however, was a young man who thought very little of himself.

How did I overcome it all? I didn't do it alone.

A college professor who took early interest in me, a peak performance coach, a girlfriend/fiancée/wife who stuck with me through it all (including some verbal abuse by a family member which would have driven away anyone who wasn't a powerful gift of love), a circle of loving friends who have valued me for close to five decades, a world class therapist I was lucky to find, and several epiphanies combined to get me to this remarkable point in my life.

As I write this, I am sixty-six years old and am ready to do great things when most are either burned out or contemplating retirement.

....

The best years of my life are right in front of me. A miracle.

....

My first tipping point occurred in college. A sociology professor took interest in me. We became friendly. I told him of my upbringing and the difficulty I had. Professor Sheldon Seller gave me his phone number and invited me to call him if I needed help. Fast forward a year or so. I had just gotten engaged to the most wonderful girl I would ever meet. One family member, for reasons I could not and never will comprehend, emphatically extended, shall we say, a less-than-warm welcome to Fran and her family, causing needless internal strife and an added layer of self-doubt in me.

....

Professor Seller talked me through a thought process which altered my self-talk for the better. It was my first lesson to never doubt my power of love and to stand for what I know is right.

....

This first step on my long journey to self-esteem, self-acceptance, and purposefulness paid off beautifully. Fran and I are happily married for over forty-two years with two beautiful children.

From childhood, my quintessential Jewish mother implanted in me the desire to be a doctor. It was, therefore, the only career I thought to pursue. Although my natural talents were verbal, I had the notion that purposefulness and meaningfulness and earning a good living would only be derived from a career in medicine. That quickly came to an end when I got rejected by twenty-three medical schools in my senior year of college. Interestingly, in that process, our college's pre-med advisor ripped me to shreds in his interview. I remember walking out of that interview thinking that I was unworthy of being a dog catcher, let alone a physician. Professor Jackson (not his real name) did write me a stellar letter of recommendation for medical school, but it was to no avail.

So I languished for two years. I worked for a retail chain for those years, moving up from stock boy to store manager. I remember wondering if this was to be my path; I was making a few dollars, saving money, and working an easy job. I soon became subject to the same barrages of verbal assault that I received at home from both our dissatisfied customers and from middle management, whose policies and procedures were woefully flawed and who needed scapegoats to deflect blame from themselves.

One summer, my best friend took me to his swim club with his family. His dad, who was my dentist, took me aside and told me to stop wasting my time and become a dentist. Dr. Bob, as I called him, loved his work, made a great living, and seemed to thrive in his office. He invited me down to observe and I was sold. Dr. Bob's passion for his work and, more obviously, for his patients was palpable. I wanted to be like Dr. Bob.

I remember the elation over my first dental school acceptance. I remember my mother crying with joy. I remember feeling, finally, validated as a person and accepted as someone who could make a difference. I envisioned myself as the next Dr. Bob: loved, talented, wealthy, and living the life. I felt empowered, no longer a slave to the retail store, its inept middle managers, and its overly demanding customers. I remember the great feeling of saying "*no*" when middle management wanted to transfer me to a store in a high-crime neighborhood. I stayed in my local store, a short walk from home, and enjoyed working until just before I got married that summer. I also remember the fun of the 1977 New York blackout, staying out all night guarding my store with my coworkers and laughing it up with other merchants on Queens Boulevard. I was on my way to getting married to the love of my young life and becoming the next Dr. Bob. I was thrilled.

Dental School Trials And Tribulations

Then dental school hit. After the initial euphoria of meeting the really interesting and nice people who would be my classmates, we sat down to some orientation lectures. It started with the "launchpad for divorce" lecture and went downhill from there. That was my introduction to the negative, authoritarian world of dental academia, where students were verbally beaten to submission in a process designed to teach us the skills necessary to fix the oral ills of the world.

I remember one of our instructors telling us that becoming a dentist is like joining a fraternity; four years of hazing followed by the Hell Night of State Board Examinations. This is how the careers of dentists have been launched. If this weren't so real, it could be the basis of a sitcom.

Let me please be clear on this: we learned a lot in school. We laughed a lot and made some pretty good friendships, some of which have lasted to this day, forty-plus years later. Many of my classmates seemed to have flourished in this environment. Some people are emotionally equipped to deal with this. To my knowledge, all of us at MCV-D '81 have become good dentists, successful in our own way. However, I do not know how they have treated their teams, their families, the people who seek their care, or, more importantly, themselves. I do not know how many divorced, suffered from depression, felt a need for authoritarianism, had disgruntled or disconnected people leave their employment or their care, or resorted to an insurance or other third-party payment method in order to save them the trouble of retaining or capturing (and I use that word intentionally) business.

You see, humility, love, and compassion toward others are every bit as important as technical talent. As we have always known and the public had discovered toward the late-1970s/early-1980s, almost everything a dentist does outside of crisis-of-the-moment care is entirely elective. Those with incredible talent who lack critical emotional and verbal skills could probably fix teeth, but could not possibly succeed in helping people get and stay well.

Edgar Schein, in his book *Humble Inquiry*, reminds us that we all need to act as though we need each other because we do. We dentists cannot fulfill our missions without the help of a clinical and administrative support team. Each member of our team needs us for a paycheck and, hopefully, for some meaningful and fulfilling work. And here's a dirty secret for you to ponder: we *all* need our patients to provide us with the opportunity to make a difference for them every bit as much as they need us for care.

If we understand this, we can learn to enrich our work, our lives, and the lives of all the souls we touch in a way that I believe doctors were intended to work. We know our team very well. We exchange snippets of our lives every day. We share in their happiness and stand with them in challenging times.

A few examples: Whenever my wife and I travel, our team always gets a little gift from wherever we go. Usually it's chocolate from a local confectioner or souvenir T-shirts for them or their children. They get flowers on their birthdays. And when they need a few hours off for a school event for one of their children, we do everything possible to adjust their schedules. We cannot do it 100 percent of the time and they understand that. But we are pretty good at doing this for them. They truly appreciate all we do and I believe we get repaid with loyalty and reciprocal dedication.

Humility also plays a role in our office policies. Cancellations and broken appointments have haunted dental practices for decades. I believe this phenomenon will continue for a very long time. Life is very busy. People's schedules are very complicated. Employers can call people to work unexpectedly. Relatives can get sick. Children and spouses can have real emergencies. And just like regular folks, we dentists and our teams can also mess up on our scheduled times.

I recently had to cancel an appointment with my trainer because my son's car broke down and I was the only person who could have helped him get to a rental car at 4:30 on a Thursday afternoon so that he could get to work the next day. If this could happen to me, a very good client for my trainer, how can I not understand when this happens to one of our loyal people in the office? I certainly do not advocate a policy of total tolerance for all cancellations and broken appointments; however, the people who truly appreciate us need to be given a little slack when life gets in the way of their seeking our care. We also may not want to be heavy-handed in a highly competitive environment where the perception of greed created by a fee for broken appointments will turn people away with resentment.

In our office, we combined love and humility with a selectively enforced policy that asks appointment breakers to make a donation to our favorite charity in exchange for rescheduling their last-minute cancellations. We enforce it very selectively and equally rarely. We really like this policy. It encourages people to respect our time. More importantly, we've gotten very good comments from people who see this. It reinforces our kind and generous nature and enhances our brand. And we've raised a few bucks for charity, turning the losing scenario of a broken appointment into the winning scenario of generosity.

A dentist once texted me (texting as a means of communication, by the way, is awful): "How do I change my feelings when I booked an hour for a patient for cleaning and the a--hole doesn't show up?" The reality is that if you're treating a--holes, perhaps a career in a branch of medicine dealing with the other end of the GI tract may be more suited for you. We need to be humble enough to realize that we are treating human beings with hearts, souls, priorities, problems, values, and limitations. We need to look first at ourselves to understand that a huge part of our task in helping people get healthier is helping them see the value of this elective service. Humility would cause us not to question the intelligence of the person who cancels, but the ability of our teams and ourselves to communicate that value in a way that each individual understands. Even then, a person may not *get it*, and that's okay. We cannot solve everyone's problem. We can, however, do our best to help them choose health and to establish that our responsibility for that person has some end point. This particular dentist would do much better if he looked closely at the value of his work; his true need for each patient; and his ability, verbiage, and systems to communicate empathy, humility, and value to those he serves.

Let's Talk About Love

Yes, I said love.

You may ask, as Tina Turner did, *what's love got to do with it?*

When I Googled the definition of the word love, I found this: compassion, care, caring, regard, solicitude, concern, warmth, friendliness, friendship, kindness, charity, goodwill, sympathy, kindliness, altruism, philanthropy, unselfishness, benevolence, brotherliness, sisterliness, fellow feeling, and humanity.

Isn't that not only what people are seeking when they come to us, but also what we ourselves are seeking from our own caregivers? Think of the best and worst medical experiences you had. What do you think of the best and worst physicians you've encountered? How do you want the people who come to you for care to feel when you're with them?

I am blessed to know some outstanding physicians who have cared for me as though I were their best friend. In some cases, the physicians were, indeed, my friends. In other cases, I've been able to create a very personal rapport with them. That rapport not only made my experience in some very frightening and uncomfortable medical scenarios (think prostate examinations in the presence of elevated PSA) way less scary; it also made me a raving fan of the amazing Simon Hall, MD.

I live two hours from Hall's practice and I travel that distance twice a year to see him. I bring a gift to him at every visit *and* have referred people from my area to him. The man took the time to properly diagnose me, spare me from needless invasive and dangerous procedures, and comforted me with the understanding that my condition is far from life-threatening. He has also saved the life of one of the people I sent to him. I have very good reason to consider Hall a friend.

In an era of rapidly increasing depersonalization and commoditization of care, wouldn't it be great if the people seeking your care emerged from each and every visit to *your* office as time spent with a friend? What would you and your team feel if, indeed, there were a loving relationship between you and everyone walking into your office? How would you feel about Monday morning if you were entering a house of love and care? The tough nature of doing good dentistry wouldn't change, but you and your team would feel a whole lot better about your hard jobs. I challenge you and your team to think about ways that each of you can create that kind of environment.

So, you think I'm crazy? Think again!

In June of 2019 I had the opportunity to hear Todd Williams speak to the Speaking Consulting Network in Kansas City. For twenty years, Williams helped develop the cultural training that developed the Four Seasons hotel chain as a leader in luxury hospitality. As of this writing, he is the vice president of culture development of Centura Health.

Williams clearly asserted that exceptional service is no longer good enough. "Lead with love," Williams said. "Put your passion first. Then present your credentials!"

We were reminded by Williams that when times are tough, love is what matters most. When we look back on the awful time during and shortly after the 9/11 attack or other times of mass crisis, our society was reduced to nothing but love. Think about what happens to families when a loved one dies. In all but the most extremely dysfunctional cases, family members cast aside their differences and *bond together*.

If Williams is correct that our most basic need is love, it follows that establishing a culture of love in your office will grow your practice, increase case acceptance, enhance your enjoyment of your life's work, and attract great people to your team.

Finally, in the litigious #metoo era, please do not confuse the concept of love of another human being with inappropriate romantic involvement or sexual harassment. It is very important that boundaries be established in *any* loving relationship. Your office is no exception. Be sure you have a written sexual harassment policy that is read and signed by everyone. It's a very sad reality in 2019 and I do not think it's going to get better any time soon.

Entering The Profession

I was fortunate enough to get into a general practice residency in New Jersey, close enough to my wife's and my hometowns to be near our aging parents. During my residency, I moonlighted in a dental office of a very successful dentist and after residency I got a fulltime job in the office of another busy practitioner. Both offices were plagued by heavy turnover of associate dentists. But for this guy of low self-esteem and lower self-efficacy, the shelter of a pseudo-patriarchal, dominant boss who, overtly and subliminally, showed me that I couldn't possibly succeed on my own and limited the amount of work I would be permitted to do was a safe, dental school-like environment. After all, this was how I was shown that dentists became successful.

Eventually, by some miracle, I developed the strength and belief that I could open my own office. With nothing in the bank, a substantial loan, and very few connections, I opened my office. It was the beginning of a miraculous, remarkable journey of frustration, error after error, self-doubt, and struggle.

In other words, *I grew.*

I got better. I found mentors, colleagues, and friends to share my journey. I made clinical errors. I corrected them. I made some little business mistakes. I corrected them. I made *huge* business and financial errors which cost me a lot. I corrected them, too. And here I am, better, richer, and stronger than ever, with passion, drive, and belief in myself and my mission.

One can think that it's terrible that my twenty years of much-less-than-optimal growing up and my less-than-delightful entry into dentistry would take decades to correct. But those seemingly awful years saw me get an education, have a lot of fun without causing myself or others harm, make lifelong friends, including my fantastic wife, and embark on a path that got me to this point.

....

How did it all happen? I'm not sure, but I can tell you this much: By some miracle which I cannot explain, the right teachers came along when I needed them the most.

....

At age fifty-eight, I found myself thirty-five pounds overweight, living paycheck to paycheck, feeling that I failed at everything I did. I was, indeed, miserable. Acting out of fear, I sought the help of a new financial advisor, a dental practice coach, a nutritionist, and personal trainers. The financial advisor told me to sell my house. My coach showed me how to create systems to reflect my values and uniqueness. The nutritionist taught me how to fuel my body—including my brain—properly. The trainers whipped me into shape.

Seemingly, in the blink of an eye (read *in a few short years*) I found myself in great shape physically, financially, and emotionally. I inspired my wife to join me on a journey to wellness; even a few of the people I treat followed my lead and lost significant, life-threatening weight. All of a sudden, I went from being a self-doubting underachiever destined for failure to an inspirer. Diminished financial stress and a sense of mission was a springboard for my practice. Eating well and exercising made me feel great about myself. It changed my thinking so much that I decided to become a Certified Health Coach. I've taken courses on behavior change and am expanding my knowledge of health along with my dentistry. Out of the chaos that was my (seemingly) failing career came an explosion of growth and excitement, both in and out of my dental practice.

My battle to overcome a poor way of seeing myself and the world has provided me with the wisdom to see self-esteem issues in myself and others for what they are. I can now conquer these issues as they surface and can help others—especially dentists—do the same.

I've come full circle to realize that for some susceptible individuals, the dental school experience could produce *mini-me* versions of myself.

I get it.

But it doesn't have to be that way.

If we center ourselves on who we are, the reasons we are getting into dentistry (or any well intended endeavor), and a purpose-driven life, the stress of learning can be converted into a largely positive experience. We do not have to be fearful of instructors who only know the authoritarian model of teaching. We do not have to have our hearts in our throats when a margin is not perfect or occlusion is a bit off. And we do not have to shrivel if a person does not appreciate our good intentions and leaves our office. Instead, we can discipline ourselves into looking at criticism with unapologetic curiosity.

We can thank our instructors for bringing things to our attention (that'll blow their minds and maybe stimulate *them* to begin to change). We can get comfortable with our own imperfections and ask a trusted colleague for some perspective on improving our good but (always) imperfect work. And we can (selectively) apply the same unapologetic curiosity to people who leave our office with a phone call inviting them back to give us the opportunity to right whatever perceived wrong that may have upset them. What I'm saying is that if we act out of the goodness of our hearts and the sharpness of our minds at all times, we do not have to feel badly about ourselves. Bad outcomes, more often than not, can be corrected. They *never* outweigh good intentions and, more importantly, unless your actions are illegal, immoral, or unethical, they *never* bring the world to an end.

And that leads me to one more point about our profession and our colleagues: *never judge other dentists!*

That's for lawyers, judges, and regulators.

Your job is to treat people.

And *mea culpa*: I cannot tell you how many times I've seen new people in my office and wondered what their previous dentist was thinking, only to discover that I could do no better. I work very hard internally to assume that everyone is just plodding through life doing their best. Others do it differently than I do. Some are more talented than I am; some are not. With rare exception, all are simply good people, just like you and me. Work on that assumption and life will get a whole lot better. Wouldn't you want to be judged by your intentions and not by an occasional flaw?

My purpose from this day forward is to show my colleagues that the career we all have chosen is a path to fulfillment. By living with intent, focusing on bettering the lives of those who choose you to serve them, and understanding that you have so many choices on the kind of dentistry you'd like to practice, you can have a wonderful career. See yourself as you're meant to be. Let your dentistry help you define that self-vision. Maintain your sense of significance, because you are just that. Stop the poison that is comparison to others. And please have a little fun in the process.

Lesson 3

Take Off The Blinders

In the Declaration of Independence adopted on July 4, 1776, America's founding fathers made a bold assertion: "We hold these truths to be self-evident, that all men are created equal, that they are endowed by their Creator with certain unalienable Rights, that among these are Life, Liberty, and the pursuit of Happiness."

In our daily pursuit of material wealth, we can forget this critical truth about happiness.

We are not guaranteed money and we are not guaranteed happiness. We are guaranteed the right to pursue happiness. Dentistry gives us some amazing opportunities for this. Understand that there is no one formula for the ideal practice.

How-to books don't work. If they did, according to researcher Brené Brown, PhD (in her audiobook *The Power of Vulnerability*):

....

> *We wouldn't be the most obese, in debt, over-medicated,*
> *and addicted culture ever. If there was one formula for*
> *success, we would all be perfectly content.*

....

I have seen so many dentists get lost in the daily grind of fixing teeth, managing employees, paying bills, and wondering how they're going to get through the rest of their careers. I've seen brilliantly trained specialists languish in misery despite their amazing skill and potential for fulfillment in every sense of the word. I have listened to dentists complain about how life is so miserable as they get into their beautiful cars and go to their beautiful homes to their beautiful families. I've seen divorce as people face financial challenges, growth in separate directions, and disconnection with the love in their lives. I've seen the tragedy of suicide in some phenomenal, beloved dentists and have learned that we are second only to police officers and soldiers at risk of depression. I've witnessed some very talented (and some not-so-talented) dentists drown in a sea of debt. Some recovered. Some didn't.

I've also seen dentists younger than I am who are overweight, out of shape, with poor posture, and zero energy face health problems that they could have avoided. I've seen dentists spread cynicism and negative energy in their offices day in and day out, wondering why patients leave and teams turn over constantly as they work to their energy's end trying to keep afloat. These are the dentists—and their families—I worry about the most.

And I have seen dentists in every skill level and every niche from Medicaid providers to high-end cosmetic and full mouth rehabilitation love every minute of their lives. Imagine a dentist in a Medicaid or insurance-based practice enjoying life? Imagine contentment in high-pressure specialists and prosthodontists whose work is incredibly demanding and could suck the life out of them. Why do some dentists grow and some cower in the face of challenge? Why do we sometimes not realize that a stress-less life is impossible and that stress can be converted into an opportunity for growth?

And I, too, suffered from a syndrome I jokingly call PMD—Perpetually Miserable Dentist.

Cancellations *meant* the end of the world. Imperfection in my crowns and restorations *meant* that I was no good. Bite splints to treat TMD that didn't work immediately *meant* that I knew nothing. In my mind, I went bankrupt dozens of times, only to find that imagined reality never materialized. And there were Monday mornings when I dreaded getting out of bed. I was living in a place of stress and fear.

Show me a person without stress and I'll show you a cadaver.

I have spoken personally to hundreds of dentists. I've listened to their stories over almost four decades. And as I reflect over my story, I realize that I have not arrived to this wonderful point in my life by accident. I was only after I realized that, without exception, we all have our struggles and we all have our stresses. When it finally dawned upon me that I am no different than some amazing dentists I've had the honor of knowing, it occurred to me that my life is pretty darned good. And so are theirs.

It seems, as the Zen proverb states, that when the student is ready, the teacher appears. When I hit the depths of my misery, not aware that my life was not so bad, but living paycheck to paycheck, overweight, out of shape, without purpose, in debt, and wondering if my life was going to work out at all, the right people appeared in my life.

One characteristic that served me well was my desire to talk about my problems with trusted friends and colleagues. I talked about my financial issues with my respected colleague and good friend Dr. Frank Graziano who referred me to financial advisor extraordinaire, Jim DiNardo. Jim, who is *old* enough to be my son, showed my wife and me our financial reality and, with loving honesty, showed us a way out of our predicament. It was hard for us not only to listen to this very young gentleman, but also to accept and pay the price for our mistakes. We stopped living and supporting an illusion and scaled our life down to our reality. That's when the magic happened. Stress dropped. Fun increased. We were liberated from the demon of monster bills fouling up our life. We had money in the bank and were able to resume funding our retirement.

Meanwhile, my dear friend and chiropractor, Raj Gupta DC, walked up to me and noticed that I was getting a bit pudgy. I told him that I thought I was eating right. With a smirk on his face he poked a finger in my belly and said, "How's that working out for ya, Doc?" Dr. Raj, as we fondly call him, led me to a world-class nutritionist and personal trainer.

So we invested our new-found discretionary dollars in personal trainers and nutritionists and the magic continued. We learned that when you eat well, your brain changes. When your body is in shape, your self-esteem and confidence grow. Both my wife and I carry ourselves differently. We are way more positive in our outlooks and demeanors. We have our moments—life is not perfect and neither are we—but we're much more energetic, happier, and healthier. And we really like the way we look.

Gratitude Is Currency

I remember that quote from a continuing education course I took when the Great Recession of 2008 occurred. At the time, I thought it was mumbo jumbo designed to make us miserable dentists get out of touch with *reality* and spend money we don't have. I was wrong. I began thinking about my fantastic wife, my wonderful adult son and daughter, my amazing friends and mentors, and all the experiences we have accumulated. I began thinking about my mother, who rose from the depths of hell that was the Holocaust to bring my brother and me into the world and was unable to see the beauty and power of her survival. That moment of gratitude for all I have and for all I am overshadowed the doubt about what I do not have and what I am not. And as deeply as I wish I could have taught that valuable lesson to have made Mom's life better is how deeply I want *you* to understand that a good life begins with gratitude.

With my newly found health, wellness, confidence, and financial stability, I dug deep to adopt "Gratitude is Currency" as a center point of my thinking. I also know now that the health and wellness component of life is critical to my patients as it is to me. So, I will continue the insane journey that led me to become a Certified Health Coach and Behavior Change Specialist and will build on that knowledge. Wellness ties into everything good.

Out of my pain I found my own unique answers. Out of what I thought were irreversible losses and unparalleled incompetence and stupidity, I found my purpose in the world.

....

I am living by intent and see my most productive,
impactful, and rewarding years ahead of me.

....

By living in gratitude, finding purpose, establishing health, and learning to love and appreciate myself, I have changed my life and am on a mission to change people's lives for the better.

So, I ask you: Why are you here? What special gifts do you have to give to the world? How has your dentistry done that and how can you make it do better? What can you do to be healthier or stronger? What are you grateful for? How do you keep money from getting in your way? And how do you find joy, wonder, and fulfillment in the time you have here?

I am continuing to improve on my answers to those questions as I grow. From this very special place in life, when some consider retiring, I am fired up. If I can do it, you can, too. Yes, I mean *you*.

Let's go.

Lesson 4

You Can't Do It Alone

Now that we know that our work has meaning, here's a question for the people you serve given with my best New Jersey dialect and attitude: "So, what's it to ya?" (And while we're in full Jersey mode, do your patients "Got a problem with that?")

I was fortunate to have studied at the Pankey Institute in Key Biscayne, Florida. Dr L.D. Pankey, the founder of this amazing house of learning, taught that a fair fee is one which compensates us adequately *and which people pay with gratitude.* The meaning of this will be different for you than it is for anyone else. Take a look at your practice, your work, and your life. What do you want to earn? How much effort goes into providing your services? How much time? How much overhead? What will you need to earn to feel fairly compensated (not excessively and not skimpily)? What is the value of your work to the recipient—in your mind and, most importantly, in theirs? And what have you done to enhance the value of that work for the person? Some of this is clearly subjective. You will make some mistakes along the way. But if you approach your fees from this starting point, you'll be well on your way to doing great things for people and being properly rewarded, both materially and spiritually for your effort.

This important concept was presented to us before health care was considered a commodity to which all are entitled. It is more critical than ever. It's one thing to look back at the incredible impact of your work on all those around you; it's quite another to transmit that value to people seeking your services. Both are essential. You know what it takes to pay your bills, your loans, your team, and yourself.

The people you care for are not and should not be privy to that; however, what they *do* need to know is the value of what you do for them. That's another skill that our instructors never taught us. So how do we do that?

Well, it begins with *you* understanding what you're capable of. And I'm not referring to your technical prowess. You know what you're capable of and you know how to do the dentistry. I am referring to the impact of whatever you do for people. Now that you know how you create sacred moments in your office, go back and relive those moments. Next, read your online reviews to see how you've impacted the lives of others. This will give you a sense of clarity of what you mean to people, knowledge of what you've done for people, and a cause for you and your team to talk up your practice as something terrific. By the way, please have your entire team ask for online reviews so you can amass a library of them, both for marketing purposes and for internalizing the benefits of your unique and special brand of dentistry.

The next step is to ask what each person seeking care in your office wants and, more importantly, what your treatment would mean to them. Take some time with them. Reflect on their ideas, values, hopes, and possible obstacles and limitations with each one of them *before* you begin any work that goes beyond a single tooth; in other words, repeat the person's wishes, how your work would get them those things they wish for, and how it would impact their quality of life. This will help you to clearly establish and demonstrate—in your mind and theirs—that you understand what the impact of your work will be.

....

Everyone makes decisions and spends money on value.
The big point here is for you to establish that value for the
person seeking your care.

....

This will help to justify your fair fee to people.

Be sure to share that knowledge with your team.

Let it resonate as talk points between the person and each member of your team.

What you're doing is buying into the value systems of the people who are trusting you with your care. And you're showing your team that your skills are dwarfed by their impact on others.

How Does Your Team See You (And How Do You See Them)?

The first job I had as a teenager and college student were summer jobs at Pierce Country Day Camp, a very successful family-run business. Its owner, Thomas T. "Bud" Pierce, was the son of its founder and had grown the business into a serious name brand for summer recreation for children from preschool to age fourteen in the Queens and Long Island areas of New York. I was actually a camper there until age fourteen and then wanted to continue there as a worker. One of the first things Pierce said to his workers at orientation was, "Here at Pierce, you don't work for us; you work *with* us."

Pierce walked the walk of this philosophy. He knew everyone by name, always had something kind to say, and always inquired how his counselors, maintenance, transportation, and food workers were doing. There was a true sense of family at Pierce. I, along with many others, made lifelong friends during my experience there. I experienced a few very sad moments upon my acceptance to dental school because that meant that I would no longer be able to go back to my summertime happy place. I believe that the success of the Pierce organization, which is still flourishing today after 100 years in business, was that no one worked for anyone; we all worked together. Pierce was decades ahead of his time because he mastered *and taught* the concept of workplace teamwork in the sixties and seventies, decades before it became fashionable.

Leadership Styles

Leadership is a funny thing. It means different things to different people. And the way you see your role as a leader, both inside and outside of your office, will determine both the quality of people you attract and the quality of their work.

At the time of this writing, Donald Trump is the President of the United States. While we will never know what goes on behind the closed doors of the Oval Office of any administration, we do know that President Trump has a bit of difficulty holding on to key people. I would suggest that, regardless of how you feel about his policies, President Trump's style and definition of leadership is going to adversely affect the quality of the work he is doing. And I would suggest that dentists with a Trumpian style of leadership may not be able to hold on to a loyal and devoted team.

The best definition of leadership comes from my dear friends and mentors, Mary Osborne and Joan Unterschuetz. They teach that leadership is *a conversation which supports mutual growth and learning with a bias toward action.*

How do you and your team support one another's growth and learning? Do you allow your team to learn (read: *make mistakes*)? Are your team members safe to approach you with issues in their departments that need correction or are they scared to show you that they screwed up? Now, there are two sides to this coin. I am assuming that your team members are well intentioned, reasonably skilled good workers who want to grow and are mature enough to handle constructive critique. *And* I am assuming (a) that you at least understand that yelling and screaming can only result in negative emotions and will lead to a toxic work environment and (b) that you can receive input from your team about things you may not be able to see. If my two preceding assumptions are untrue, something has to change. The truth is that we need our teams as much as they need us.

Schein writes about this in *Humble Inquiry*. The world is complex, diverse, and interdependent. Schein emphatically tells of the importance of asking questions and forming relationships based on mutual respect and the recognition that others know things that we may need to know in order to do our work. Humble inquiry is not the sharing of our deepest secrets to people who work in our office. It is, however, a sincere curiosity and interest about the lives and affairs of others around you. It is a willingness to listen generously with the understanding that we need our teams in order to accomplish our life's work every bit as much as they need us to accomplish theirs. So how much do you know about the lives of your assisting, hygiene, and administrative teammates? How much do they know about yours? Are you close and cohesive enough to feel safe with one another? Why is this important? It turns out that in critical mishaps like the *Challenger* space shuttle tragedy or nuclear power plant accidents, subordinates had information which could have prevented or mitigated the consequences of these incidents. They withheld the information either because they didn't feel safe bringing uncomfortable news to the boss or they perceived that their input was never taken seriously. Take down the authoritarian barriers. Listen generously. Develop a togetherness mindset. Your practice will accomplish so much more.

If you can take a close look at yourself and create policies, philosophies, and a culture that caters to your happiness, money and freedom will *follow* in more than ample quantity.

What Is Freedom?

At a get-together with a few families we're close to, the subject of freedom came up. The definition and terms and conditions of freedom became very elusive. After all, I do not have the freedom to walk into my bank and take the contents of its vault home with me. And you do not have the freedom to tell your bank, your landlord, and your creditors that you don't feel like paying your bills this month.

So, what is freedom and when do you actually experience it? A number of years ago, I took some flying lessons to put an end to my fear of flying. Piloting a single engine Cessna demanded my total attention to every single detail of that aircraft and my surroundings from the moment I approached the plane until I tied it down at the flight school. There was no time for fear or any other distraction from the many tasks at hand; any small error could be catastrophic.

So, when I was flying, *nothing else* existed in my life. I watched the instruments, the airspace around me, taking in the beautiful optics of the world around me, focusing on where I was, and what that Cessna was doing. I was totally immersed in my flying to the exclusion of all else and loving it all. I was free.

....

Freedom, I believe, is being engrossed in an effort you enjoy that is worthwhile. Dentistry offers us so many opportunities for freedom.

....

We have procedures which will benefit others that demand our total focus and attention. We have people in our offices, from team to patients, to the UPS guy, who benefit from our generous listening to them. We have a community we could influence with our work. All we need to do is to use our unique talents to the best of our ability. My questions to you are: Who are you? What do you enjoy about dentistry? What are your unique talents? And how can you apply those talents to immerse yourself in your work, and gain inner satisfaction, freedom, and get paid for it?

In other words, sit down and find your purpose in life and in practice. Find your unique *why*. If you can do that—if your actions in practice, and in life, are consistent with your core values—you will be happy, you will be free, and you will make enough money to live your preferred life.

Who Are You?

Your vision of a good practice and life is as unique to you as mine is to me. Take a look around yourself. What do you see? Do you like it? What would you like to change? What would you like to remain the same? What dental procedures are you doing? What are you really good at? What do you enjoy doing? What clinical skills would you like to improve or learn? Take a few moments to reflect on this and write down your thoughts. Start to focus on those things you enjoy doing. Take more Continuing Education courses in these areas. See if you can apply those skills to the people you see every day. Set some SMART goals (we'll talk more specifically about SMART goals later) to focus you on doing more of what you like. If you're caught in a whirlwind of a too-busy practice, you could designate a half or a full day a week as *doing the dentistry I love* hours. Watch the magic happen. And if you can't stand doing certain things, delegate or refer them.

What about life outside your practice? Do you have a vision of what you'd like your life to look like? Where do you want to live? What kind of community would satisfy you and your family? Do you need to be near a particular faith-based community or a house of worship? What are your favorite leisure activities? Are there places you'd like to visit? Things you'd like to own? Most importantly, please give thought to your role as a spouse, parent, son/daughter, sibling, and friend. Carve out time and budget some money for all of this. In your early years or if finances are a factor, you don't have to spend a lot of money. Just carve out some time for personal development, fun, and love. In other words, live a little. Have you ever thought about the legacy you'd like to leave behind? What would you like people to say about you when you're gone? Live into the future by creating it in writing. Look at your thoughts regularly. Modify them as you grow and change. Remember, nothing is etched in stone. The point is to see what you want to do and who you want to become and move toward it.

Feed yourself with your dreams but don't take the poison. Once we decide to enter a profession, we begin to feel the competitive pressure that is needed in order to get into a good college, dental school, and, perhaps a specialty program. We feel the need to maintain grades that are better than most and often look at others' grades to gauge our chances of landing in the schools and programs of our choices. We live in a culture of comparison, in which winners of sports or entertainment awards are idolized. By the time we get out of dental school, we are obsessed with comparing our practice, our work, our homes, our cars, and our money with (what seem to be) our peers' assets. This is the worst form of personal poison we can feed ourselves. It's based on nothing rational and has the incredible potential to lead you down the primrose path of depression and poor self-esteem.

The truth is that no one has any basis for comparison to anyone else. The truth is that you have no idea what price someone else paid and is paying for their house, car, clothes, etc. The truth is that you have no idea how good, bad, or ordinary anyone else's practice or work is. And the truth is that none of these things have *anything* to do with your worthiness in any role you play in life.

Many times, while raising my kids, I called into serious question my ability to provide for them as compared to some of my colleagues and contemporaries. All too often I felt inadequate as a parent and family provider. I wished I could have given Neil and Tracey some of the stuff that other kids had. But my reality testing of these thoughts was totally false. The truth of all this came out a few years ago when my daughter, Tracey, who had moved out at age twenty-three to share a home with a few friends, told us how much she appreciated her upbringing.

"I hear stories from my friends about how messed up their childhood homes were," says Tracey. "I never realized how normal my mom and dad are and how good I had it growing up."

You are unique. Everything you do is a result of things that make you different than anyone else. Your home, your practice, and your relationships will reflect who you are, and that is *not bad*. As long as your actions are consistent with who you are and are legal, moral, and ethical, it is more than unreasonable to use another person as a benchmark for your own success or worthiness in any aspect of your life. Get one thing straight over and above anything else: no matter what you have or have yet to accomplish; *no matter how good, great or amazing your dentistry is; no matter what condition you're in, you are worthy of love, respect, and belonging. And the first person whose love and respect you must win is yours.*

How much respect do you have for all the tangible and intangible things you have achieved? How much respect do you have for who you really and truly are? And please don't confuse a desire to improve with respect for who and what you are.

I have a team member who had a habit of throwing her back and the palms of her hands against the corridor walls of my office as I walked past her. When I questioned why she would do that, Esther would tell me, "That's how I was raised." I have asked her to please stop doing that and have initiated several discussions about respecting herself and losing the authoritarian model of dentistry and of life. Esther is learning the lesson I learned much later in my life than she is in hers. I hope that when she looks at her time on our team, she will have received more than a batch of paychecks from us.

In his book, *Love Yourself Like Your Life Depends On It,* author Kamal Ravikant teaches: "The truth is to love yourself with the same intensity you would use to pull yourself up if you were hanging off a cliff by your fingers."

If, like many people, you didn't have the good fortune of entering adulthood with self-love and respect, all is not lost. These qualities *can* be learned by reading about and focusing on them.

A good therapist, peak performance coach, or simply a life coach can help you get these *critical* qualities of success. Set your own standards. See yourself as you're meant to be and live a life that's consistent with who you are. Build the foundation of your life on your need for love and belonging and go from there. Let *no one* set that standard for you. And the only comparison to make in any aspect of your life would be to yourself. Simply be a bit better tomorrow than you are today. That is a very healthy comparison. And please teach this to your children, too, as you teach them to love and respect themselves.

The Dirty E Word

One of the dirtiest words I know is expectation. I have learned that expectations are merely disappointments waiting to happen. Please don't be disheartened if some things that you want don't materialize immediately. Be flexible and re-evaluate your goals if they don't materialize. Put your goals in the perspective of a good, purposeful, and balanced life with full knowledge that you're doing great things every single day. And never forget the love and support that surrounds you.

Control Your Stress

Dentistry is a stressful profession. This stuff is hard. Every generation of dentists faces unique challenges and they seem to get tougher almost daily.

Stress can take a serious toll on us if we are not careful.

Additionally, we dentists are only second to police officers and soldiers at risk of depression and suicide. I have seen and read of too many outstanding dentists taking their own lives. What I learned about stress in a dental office or in life saved my sanity.

When something goes wrong in the office, strange things can happen. Our brain's amygdala, the fight-or-flight center, kicks in and puts us in an offensive or defensive mode of thinking. While our amygdala is very important in helping us survive a true life-and-death emergency, it can often misinterpret the stress that occurs in everyday life and create what Daniel Goleman, in his landmark book *Emotional Intelligence*, called an emotional hijacking. If you can create an awareness of this in the heat of the moment of any given stress, you can calm yourself and put it all in perspective.

Look at a problem you are facing now. Is it business or personal? Give it some perspective by assigning it a value on a scale of 1-100. I consider (God forbid) the death of a child a personal 100 and the simultaneous mass resignation of my team and a letter of foreclosure a business 100. Where does a disgruntled person, a shy crown margin, or a power outage in your office fall on this scale? Where does your child bringing home a less-than-ideal grade fall on the personal scale? Are you willing and able to subrogate these challenges to the amount of joy, love, and achievement you have in your life? In other words, get a clear, rational perspective on your challenges, see them for what they are, and deal with them as calmly as you can.

Amy Cuddy, in her book *Presence,* cites studies that show that your body posture directly influences your mood, your comfort, and your ability to manage problems with inner strength and confidence. When faced with a tough clinical case, case presentation, or a challenging person, I have found it helpful to sit or stand upright, shoulders back, arms away from my sides, chest out, and chin up for one to two minutes before encountering the challenge. It is amazing what this does to the brain. Try it for yourself and see how your mood and self-image change.

And if your efforts to manage stress do not succeed, please seek professional help. There is no shame in the person with debilitated teeth seeking your help; please eradicate any shame in seeking the help of a therapist if you need to do so. It could save the quality, and perhaps the quantity, of your life.

In the depth of my doubt of my self-efficacy, I sought the help of a therapist. I am grateful to this day to the late, great Arnold Lazarus, PhD, a direct disciple of Albert Ellis, PhD, who taught me the things I just mentioned. I am so grateful to have looked at my vulnerability in the eye, sought help, and found this wonderful man, whose influence in my life lives on. Later on, Peak Performance Coach Dana Ackley, PhD helped me apply my knowledge in my interactions in the office. He introduced me to Emotional Intelligence and helped me establish that as a tool to know myself and to hire a good team.

Look in the mirror every day and see yourself as you're meant to be. Get that vision in your head every day and conduct yourself as that person. Feel good about it all. Control your stress, carry yourself with inner and outer confidence, and wear a smile on your face as often as possible.

Hang Out With The Right Crowd

Associating with people of like mindset is more than valuable; it is essential for us to thrive. With so many choices on practice models out there and so many different niches, styles, and philosophies of practice, finding a good peer group of similar practitioners makes a huge difference in preserving our passion and energy for what we do. Bear in mind, as well, that we all face similar challenges. Having a sense of not being alone is so important in preventing burnout, feelings of inadequacy, depression, and—God forbid—self destruction. In their outstanding book *Younger Next Year*, Chris Crowley and Henry Lodge stress the importance of social connectedness in remaining healthy, viable, and sexy (yes, they said sexy) into our eighties and beyond. I think it's safe to say that a large number of dentists will be working well past the age of sixty-five, whether out of financial necessity or out of a need to maintain a purposeful, productive existence. If we are going to be productive vibrant, sexy (yes, *sexy*) dentists into our seventh or even eighth decades, we need to pay attention to this principle. Dental society meetings are nice because they give you bits of wisdom and some small level of camaraderie with your professional neighbors and your favorite specialists. Your national and state ADA components will also provide support in some areas of the business of dentistry. But there is nothing like a group of dentists with similar practice models and niches to fuel the fire of your mission. If you love esthetics, organizations like AACD would more likely give you the support and encouragement you need to face your challenges. If comprehensive care is your passion, names like Pankey, Spear, Kois, and Dawson come to mind. If functional medicine is your thing, AAOSH will guide and direct you through this great adventure. The colleagues you meet in these groups give generously and receive abundantly.

And there are countless local study clubs across the nation dedicated to a huge diversity of thinking and practice. Look for one. Attend a meeting. Meet people. Share experiences. Get involved. You will come out with new ideas, new energy, a very important sense of validation, and new colleagues with whom to share your triumphs and challenges. And if you love politics, your component and local societies give you countless opportunities to influence your communities and beyond.

There are also countless Facebook and online communities at your fingertips. The behavior-technical fusion of the Pankey Institute, the Oral Systemic connection advocated by AAOSH, and the diverse pursuit of excellence in my local Seattle study club keep me going. And my most recent entry into the Speaking Consulting Network showed me an enhanced level of generosity and abundance. And in my sixties, I have the curiosity and enthusiasm of a new practitioner and the experience to contribute my experience to those who seek it. Here's the key to any study group: it needs to be a safe environment for open discussion, vulnerability, and mutual support. The right study club will encourage and support you in discussing issues that perplex you or areas where you would like to grow. They're out there.

You Are What You Absorb

One word of caution: there are many dentists (and non-dentists) who seem to thrive on gloom-and-doom talk. They talk poorly about their patients, their practices, their dental colleagues, their lives, and of course, themselves. Call them complainers, whiners, victims, or Debbie Downers (remember her from *Saturday Night Live*?). They will suck the life out of you as they enter their high-end cars and drive to their McMansions on their way to vacation in the next exotic location.

....

Avoid these energy suckers like the plague. Stay with people who are supportive of themselves and of others.

....

And, incidentally, if you see yourself or catch yourself in these moments, you can change your attitude. I did, and I will tell you that the *new me* is having a lot more fun than the *old me* had.

In the areas of health and wellness, a good peer group is also important. If you are looking to lose weight or to attain an enhanced level of fitness, a gym is the obvious first step. Get to know the gym staff. See if you can either go to the gym with a partner and/or make some acquaintances there. Comfort and belonging are recurrent themes in everything we do and will make going to the gym much easier and more fun. You'll find that you can get and give support and encouragement with the people in your gym.

While we're on the subject of gyms, let's go to some vulnerability. There is no one I respect more in the gym than the overweight, out-of-shape lady or gentleman making an effort to be well. My health coaching study has taught me that out-of-shape people may be initially very self-conscious about going to a gym (perceived to be) full of in-shape folks. I know this is a real phenomenon, and if it applies to you, please talk about it openly with a coach, a trainer, or even a trusted friend. You may even see a need to do some conditioning in the privacy of your home, and that's OK too. I guarantee you that there will be many people in all sizes and shapes in the gym and it is very likely that you'll find some of your fitness peers with whom you can form a mini support community.

My gym experience has shown me that the fit ladies and gentlemen who can do things that may appear intimidating to you will never condescend you and may well provide you with some unexpected encouragement. I was grossly out of shape when I started exercising. I try to give a look or a word of encouragement to the beginners in my gym whenever I think it will help. And when *you* feel great about your condition, pay it forward to some newbie who may enter your gym. Community is important. Always remember, as well, that the goal is not to be like anyone else; just be a bit better each day.

You Can't Do It Alone

It is impossible to fulfill your mission without the right team at your side. Earlier we talked about team development. But having the *right* team in place is critical. When I came back from my first experience at the Pankey Institute and learned that our practice model was the equivalent of a boutique shop vs a large retail store, my long-time hygienist held her nose up and told me that she doesn't shop at boutiques. She resisted our efforts to reshape our practice. I did not want to let her go and I waited way too long to do so, but it eventually happened. The point here is that your team has to share your values and become vested in the success of the practice. If they are not on board, they and you will be miserable. Refer to the section on letting people go and move on.

Hiring is an art. It is not a science. The same holds true for interviewing. When I find a candidate who interviews well, I add one more critical step. I did an Emotional Intelligence Quotient (EQ) many years ago with industrial psychologist Dana Ackley, who also did some peak performance coaching for me. Any candidate I'm seriously considering will go through a similar test to see if that person's EQ complements mine and the culture of our practice. Some people like other forms of personality inventory, and that is fine. The big point here is that a few hundred dollars invested in hiring the right person can save you many thousands of dollars in replacement cost and immeasurable aggravation in the event of a bad hire. I know this because I thought I was smarter than the EQ test on two occasions. The results were very painful. Conversely, the security and joy of hiring the right person who shares your values and can complement the skills you have to offer is huge. When you assemble *your* team, energize them, train them, and focus them on a mission, Monday morning will be a good thing.

Put all these components together, live in the moment of the work you love, with and for the people you love. Be thankful for everything. Put it all in perspective. The result: the freedom you and all of us seek.

Lesson 5

Find Your Life Beyond
The Chair

While it is very important to be extremely focused on your vision and goals for your practice, we also must focus on other aspects of life. Pankey taught us that life is a balance of work, play, love, and worship. Although I have found that balance to be a struggle, it is not an unpleasant one. Family comes first. When I first started my practice, I worked six days and three nights a week, dividing my time between my office and a large corporate practice fifty miles from home. My wife worked three days in the office with me as my only employee. My son Neil was eighteen months old. There was not much money available and time was certainly at a premium.

But Friday nights were Neil and Daddy time.

We'd go to the local mall to Friendly's, eat simple food, share an ice cream dessert, and then go on the twenty-five-cent children's mechanical horse (well, Neil did that while I watched). Three decades later, Neil and I still talk about those times, especially when we take an evening together at a Jimmy Buffett concert. Understand that you do not need a lot of money to create very special memories, but you do need time. Please set time aside for your children. The rewards are huge and they last a lifetime.

Your spouse or significant other is your other main source of love. Save time and energy for that very special person who is at your side.

If you both work, designate a date night or perhaps a Sunday brunch. It doesn't have to be elaborate or expensive. All you need is some quality alone time for maintaining a deep connection. Talk about important stuff. Share your aspirations, progress, fears, and successes. Plan your future with excitement and share your vision of a great life and grow together. *Nothing* is more sacred than your family.

A good social life outside of dentistry is very helpful.

Brené Brown is a well-known researcher on shame and vulnerability. In her work, Brown tells stories trials and tribulations of her difficult youth. She was somehow able to use her struggles as a springboard to seek the knowledge and provide us with ways to overcome shame and embrace vulnerability.

Brown tells us repeatedly that every one of us has an irreducible need for love and belonging. People of similar demographic and values outside of dentistry will give you and your family just that. Cultivate friendships in your community, houses of worship, neighborhood, play groups, and clubs.

Cultivate Interests And Hobbies

We can never explore every fascinating thing about life, but one of the great things about our profession is that it offers us the opportunity to pursue other interests. From listening to music to painting to traveling the world, there is something cool to do on any budget that will pique anyone's interest. For me, my dental skills are very useful at solving little mechanical things at home, but that's about as far as I want to go with my mechanical skills.

I have used my leadership and speaking skills for the betterment of my community. I was one of a group of doctors who stopped our county from building an ill-conceived garbage incinerator in our densely populated town. We debated county officials and industrial "experts." My colleagues and I used our titles assertively but with decency and integrity. We won and had a ton of fun.

I have also worked my way through synagogue leadership and was in the unenviable position of being president of two once-rival synagogues which needed to merge out of financial and demographic necessity. Once again, my knowing my own *why* and acting out of passion turned my love of public speaking into a huge gain for my community.

Community involvement is awesome. You meet like-minded people from many backgrounds and walks of life. You get to establish your own brand as a person and as a business owner with a unique philosophy. And you get a sense of contributing to something that is much bigger than any one person. One caution about community activity: political activity has become very toxic and has the potential to alienate and hurt people once known as the loyal opposition. Today, I would advise any independent business owner or healing professional to avoid any conspicuous political activity, as many people will shun others who do not think like they do. Some people who may want to seek your wonderful care may misinterpret your political views as antagonistic to them. A leader who has the skill to bring together people of different philosophies, find common ground, and build on it would have a huge positive impact, but this would require a lot of energy and more than a wee bit of risk.

There are many creative outlets you can pursue. Some of my dental colleagues have taken up musical instruments, art, photography, racing cars, and sports. I have found a lot of fun in speaking, writing (obviously), fitness, and discovering new ways to use my talents in different areas of life. I spent some time taking flying lessons, which I wrote about in a previous chapter. My wife and I are avid New York Yankees baseball fans. We spend a lot of time going to baseball games in as many stadiums as possible and watching and talking Yankees baseball. And I will confess that we are in love with the shows, restaurants, and people watching that make up Las Vegas. What activity gives you pleasure? What non-dental things are you curious about? Set a bit of time aside weekly for it, have a little fun, and express yourself.

Lesson 6

Good Help Is Hard To Find

By now I hope you realize that no one accomplishes anything alone. It's impossible to focus on all aspects of life without losing focus on your special talents and unique purpose.

Who are the leaders in your office? I submit that each team member needs to be a leader in his or her own way. The practice owner is clearly the CEO of the entire operation. But the office manager, receptionist, patient coordinator, hygienist, and assistants are leaders in their sub-domains of your office. If they don't know this, let them know it!

Train them. Nurture them. Allow for a continuing education budget so they can take courses, either with the team or on their own, so they can develop their skills.

If you've hired the right people, trust them to make decisions to get their job done and make them feel safe, not only in reporting problems in their departments, but also in seeking your help and the help of the rest of the team when they hit a snag. They will. So will you. Few of us solve 100 percent of our issues 100 percent independently. And please do not micromanage. It only leads to resentment and increasing codependence, which leaders cannot have.

Team Building

So how do we get from having employees to having enthusiastic, loyal, and safe team members? Let's start with the best definition I heard of a team from former Procter & Gamble Executive, Bruce Manchion: "A team is a group of people learning and growing interdependently with similar goals on a common mission."

Do you have a mission statement? A common mission, with which *all* members of your team align, is critical. Once you have a mission statement, post it prominently for everyone who enters your office to see. I found it very helpful to rewrite our office's mission statement a few years ago with my team's input. It's framed in a prominent area in our reception area. We each have copies of it to read every morning in our huddle. We have it in our tissues. It unites us and gets us focused on our *why* every single day.

Invest In Your assets

I recently came across a news item that told of a small Chicago restaurant announcing that it will add a 4 percent surcharge to bills in order to help pay for its employees' health insurance and to raise the wages of its kitchen staff. I love this. Restaurant workers are not so high on the pay scale and restaurants are extremely volatile businesses running on very tight margins. An *entrepreneur* is defined as a risk-taker. Here is an entrepreneur taking a risk that his patrons will see his action as one of decency toward the people who make their dining experience enjoyable. In a tight labor market, this action would also attract and keep good people. The publicity the owner is getting is making him look not only like a good guy in the world of business, but also like a highly desirable employer. The story mentioned that the owner will not force his patrons to pay the surcharge. This guy is smart, transparent, and decent. If I were living in Chicago, I would be a regular there (providing, of course, that they serve some healthy stuff on their menu) *and* I'd gladly pay the 4 percent for the hard-working folks who help create an enjoyable dining experience.

We have an advantage in dentistry because we pay far more than a restaurant does and our margins are nowhere near as tight as those of a restaurant. But we still need to offer more than a paycheck and, perhaps, other benefits if we are to attract and retain great people. Some of the things we can offer our teams include: continuing education locally or by webinar; opportunity to interact with peers through study clubs; team outings (it doesn't have to be elaborate); participation in national conferences (for practices that can afford to do so); flexible hours for family time; and, simply saying thank you at the end of the day or extending a compliment for a task or job well done.

What do *you* do to enhance your team's job satisfaction? And how do you market this to your clientele and to the dental community?

One final note: Herb Kelleher, the late Chairman of Southwest Airlines, turned a small, three-aircraft regional airline into one of the largest carriers in the United States that challenges its three large competitors every day. One of Kelleher's secrets was to put his employees first. He knew their names, their birthdays, their happiness, and their sorrows. He encouraged them to be themselves and maintain a sense of humor as they worked very hard to build the organization. The result is a (relatively) pleasant flying experience with low prices, few frills, and a lot of smiles.

....

Put your team members first. They will know and appreciate that and will act in the best interest of the practice and those it serves with the same enthusiasm and passion as yours.

....

And they'll go the extra mile for you.

Allow Them To "Fail"

No one is perfect. No one does their job to 100 percent accuracy 100 percent of the time. Not even you, doctor. So, let's put some things in perspective. Once again, let's assume that your team is smart, loyal, and dedicated to the practice and its mission. And let's assume that someone on your team committed an egregious error. One of my favorite ones is the front desk person scheduling someone and failing to put that person in the schedule. When that person shows up, I want to scream, don't you? Let's realize that, although screaming is an option, it may not lead to desirable results (especially in my case where the front desk person is my wife). How would you feel about squashing that scream desire, taking a deep breath, pausing a moment, and saying: "I'm curious how that person could have been booked that way. What do you think happened? How can I or the team help you prevent it?" The reality of life is that, without exception, we are all vulnerable. More often than not, we view our vulnerability as a sign of weakness. The above language acknowledges vulnerability, embraces it, and allows a person to show it without fear of judgment. If you can see that and allow your terrific team members to discuss their vulnerability, the end result will be a much stronger team. The concept is so simple, but we so often see a nuisance as the end of the world and react in a way that helps no one. Take your team's flaws, address them openly and without threat, and turn them into growth opportunities. And stop beating yourself up over your own mistakes (yes, you make them and yes, you beat yourself up) and open yourself up to input from caring others. Getting to know your team, allowing them to know you, creating an environment of empathy, curiosity, and common mission will go a long way in ensuring optimal function and happiness in your life's work.

While we're on this subject, let's circle back to the authoritarian model of dentistry and life and how it affects our teams. History is filled with stories of protest and dispute. At the time of this writing, the airport in Hong Kong is closed due to citizens protesting for democracy. Labor unions were created because employees were besieged by business owners and governments unilaterally imposing tougher-than-necessary conditions on hard-working people. And, in turn, labor unions exploited their positions of power by having workers work by union rules rather than the betterment of the business or government. When power is wielded in one direction, a resistance in the opposite direction will necessarily ensue. And when that happens, there will be pain. There will be winners and there will be losers. Do we really need that in our daily lives when there is a better way?

Remember this definition of leadership: *a conversation designed for mutual learning and growth with a bias toward action.* And the definition of team: *a group of people working and growing interdependently with similar goals on a common mission.* When power and authoritarianism reign, there is often a lack of true leadership and a needless tension that never works in the best interest of the team. While it is true that the practice owner is ultimately responsible for the workings of the practice, the team is essential for those workings. And the more the team feels wanted, respected, happy, and proud, the more they will be eager to go the extra mile for the practice, its mission, its owner, and all who enter.

Your team sees things you don't. Patients talk to them when you're not in the room. Assuming you've hired the right people who are vested in your unique mission, your team wants the same things you do. If they see you as a walled-off authoritarian figure who gives orders and expects obedience, Monday morning will not be something they look forward to. Instead of an authoritarian *boss versus worker* model, why not work in a collaborative model? Why not have each member of the team the team vested in everyone's success?

Interviewing and hiring are arts, not sciences. Even the best established effective hiring practices are imperfect and will occasionally give us people who are not ideal for our practices. In spite of that, it is a whole lot better to use as much science and as little guesswork as possible. I have learned a few simple and a few not-so-simple tricks to giving myself the best chance of getting the right people for my practice.

First, get written resumes from each candidate. Look at their grammar, spelling, and punctuation. This gives you an idea of the candidate's attention to detail. Some offices like to have the manager screen applicants on the phone, and that's OK. As a small practitioner, I like to do the screening myself in person. I look for body language, posture, and eye contact. Asking open-ended questions is very good, but asking candidates to tell stories is even better. For example, "Tell me a story about how you solved a clinical problem," or, "Tell me about how you successfully handled an irate patient," or, "Tell me a story about something you loved doing in your previous jobs or in school." Let the candidate express him or herself and gauge the story and the quality of their communication. You can ask about their vision of the ideal practice, ideal team, and ideal leader. You can also ask about their vision of ideal care for people. Listen and learn whether the candidate's philosophy is similar to yours. Above all, make sure the candidate is a nice person. *That really matters.*

The final revealing question I like to ask is: "What would you like to ask me about the position?" If their first questions are about bonuses, vacations, and time off, that tells me something different than if their first questions are about opportunities for growth, your philosophy of care, and continuing education. And, of course, if they're checking their cell phones during their interview, that is a red flag.

After You Hire 'Em, Train 'Em

Once you determine that a candidate is right for your office, the real work begins. I learned over time that we need to assume that every person is plodding through life as best they can. Spend time showing them your unique way. Take a little time to let them know your little quirks as well as how your philosophy translates into action. Let them take that knowledge and run with it and please do not try to micromanage them. The best assistants, hygienists, and administrators will make mistakes. Let them! Use those mistakes as learning opportunities. Make sure that they can come to you if they think they screwed up. Ask them how you or the team can help them do their job better. Meet with them regularly for short periods of time to review the past week or so.

One thing I insist on in my clients and in my life: I will *never, ever* say something negative about one team member to another. I will *never, ever* allow any other team member to do it, either. The rule is that we will not say anything about anyone behind their back that we wouldn't say to their faces. It is vital to have a culture of support and trust.

And a special word to those of us who have our spouses in the office: my wife has been at our front desk for all but two of the years I've been in practice. She behaves like a team member. The team knows that she is my wife, but that's about the only thing that differentiates her from our assistant and hygienist. If we all see ourselves as people working and growing interdependently with similar goals on a common mission, our spouses can be enormous assets to us. If your spouse cannot see himself/herself on an equal ground with the rest of the team, the spouse may unintentionally hurt the team.

Safe Space

Sooner or later, a team member who is consistently not performing well or not responding to training or instruction will hurt your office and everyone in it. In *Leadership Secrets of Colin Powell*, author Oren Harari explains the General's philosophy of letting people go when necessary. It is very important, especially in the first ninety days, to exchange ideas with new hires. Give and receive comments on how they and you are doing. Correct issues quickly and nicely, explaining the *why* as much as the *what* of the things that need correction. Be open to each team member's comments. Do it privately and in a safe space. Be patient, kind, but firm in your standards, but also be open minded to their observations.

If, after extensive training and attempts at correction, things are not working out, you must let people go. It is stressful and unpleasant, but you, your team, and your patients will suffer if the wrong team members are kept on. And the longer you let things simmer, the bigger the problem will become. If you need to let someone go, please be sure to be in compliance with federal and state labor laws. Document all interactions with team members. Consult your attorney. Some state dental associations provide this type of guidance for its members. Whenever possible, keep it as non-negative as possible. If you think you can help someone who doesn't fit in your office culture find another position, offer to do so.

It is a very poor idea to speak ill of anyone and this applies to those you have let go. Simply let your office team know that you had to make the decision to let a person go. Let patients know that the dismissed team member and you decided to part ways. Labor laws may also hold you liable for any negative comments you may make to any prospective employer. I had to let go an assistant who, over a short period of time, became rude, arrogant, and disrespectful to my patients and me.

About a year later, an FBI agent flashed his badge at my front desk and asked to speak to me. The agent informed me that he was doing a background check on this particular assistant, who was applying for a job at the newly formed TSA. The agent clearly and unambiguously informed me that I would be legally liable for anything I would say to him. My response to him was that the only thing I was comfortable disclosing were the dates of her hiring and termination and her starting and ending salaries and that I had no further comment. The agent thanked me and moved on. Your evaluation of a team person is subjective. A person doing poorly at your office may flourish elsewhere. When speaking of others, try to take the high road at all times. Your team will see you in a very positive light. They will know that, no matter what, you won't besmirch their reputations. And if you behave that way, they will likely act in kindness. Keeping negativity and negative comments out of your life is applicable all the time.

Specialists Are Team Members Too

There is no shame in referring to specialists. They are here to make you look very smart for having referred to them. I will confess that, no matter how hard I have tried, I am very slow and not very good at endodontics. I do not enjoy surgery. I also get very stressed doing both of these things. Endo and surgery have neither been profit centers nor sources of fulfillment for me, so why would I even try doing them? I have a few fantastic endodontists and surgeons near me who are truly grateful to take the burden off me. They make the people I send to them very happy and set me up to restore the affected teeth or surgical sites they have treated. Some of them even refer people to me for their dentistry. That's a three-way win: the person being treated gets the best care; the specialists have a great referral source; and I get a reduction in stress and some new people in my practice.

If your practice is large enough, you can hire an associate to do the work you don't enjoy. You can also take the opportunity to mentor your associate and enable him/her to grow into the practitioner that you've become. It could be a great win-win in the right practice. A large enough practice can also hire an endodontist, orthodontist, or oral surgeon to come to the office to do specialty work. The big questions to ask in either of these scenarios are whether the associate or hired specialist has the skill, temperament, and values that will fit into your office culture *and* whether you have the temperament to relinquish control of some procedures to an associate or specialist in an office with your name on the door.

A bartender friend of mine taught me that if you love what you do you never have to work a day in your life. So if you can identify your unique talents, you can build your day-to-day life around what you do well and what you enjoy. In other words, you can go into your office and pursue your freedom and happiness every day. That is not to say that every day will be blissful; however, when we enjoy what we do, the inevitable stresses become less significant and way more manageable.

If you are a specialist, please take heed of the following story: About twelve years ago I started doing Invisalign. For me it was fun, low stress, and profitable. The people I was treating loved seeing their results with no braces. I discussed this in a study club with an orthodontist, who ripped me to shreds and questioned my qualifications in front of our study club colleagues for doing it. Another local orthodontist invited a group of general dentists to dinner to discuss troubleshooting Invisalign cases and offered to help us any way he can. Guess who gets my complex ortho-perio-restorative cases? Can you guess who doesn't? There is an abundance of dentistry to do. Don't fall into the scarcity/competition mindset that plagues our society and our profession. Support your colleagues any time you can. Gain a reputation as a giver, an educator, and a do-gooder. You'll love your work even more and you'll garner the love and respect of your colleagues.

Bottom line: the restorative or general dentist and their specialists need to work interdependently (we need them as much as they need us) with similar goals (specialty care to preserve teeth and health) on a common mission (the care of another human being). You are all on the same team.

Lesson 7

Create The Blueprint And Watch It Grow

O K. Your blinders are off; you have an idea of who you are; you see yourself as you're meant to be; and, you are ready to rock the world. Let's create a vision and get excited about it.

First, exactly how much money would you like to earn? Do *not* compare yourself to anyone else. Do not say that you want to earn as much as Dr. Smith. Create your own salary goal and, more importantly, write down what that money will enable you to do. Keep in mind the classic question: *how much is enough?*

Let's take a look at the best way to earn that money. Create your definition of a well-restored patient. What conditions need to be fulfilled in order for someone to be healthy? Look carefully at periodontal health, occlusal health, as well as tooth-by-tooth health. Of course, if there are areas in which you would like more knowledge, identify the sources of that knowledge that are available to you.

Regardless of how great you are—and *you* are great—no one is all things to all people.

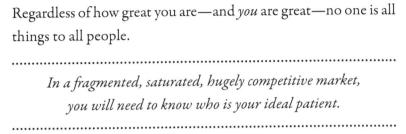

In a fragmented, saturated, hugely competitive market, you will need to know who is your ideal patient.

Break it down by age, gender, education level, household income, and health consciousness. Be aware that people who cater to more and less healthy, educated and non-educated, and wealthy or non-wealthy demographics can do well. McDonald's and Ruth's Chris Steak House are both very good businesses. All you need to know is which type of person *you* are most comfortable serving.

Congratulations, you've outlined everything you need for a good life in and out of the office. Your blinders are off. You see yourself as you're meant to be. You've got a vision in mind. And you are excited. Let's start building.

Create A Mission Statement

The best way to bring your vision to life is to write a mission statement, or statement of purpose. You can do this for your office and for your life. The importance of this cannot be overemphasized.

A mission statement gets you focused on your values at the beginning of every day. It keeps you and your team accountable to the standards you have set. And It reinforces the uniqueness of your practice to everyone who enters your office (or your life). I have done this several times in my career, changing it as I grew and as my life and practice changed.

At the beginning of my career, I wanted to be all things to all people. Our mission included all phases of dentistry for all family members, 24/7 emergency care, and energy-wasting effort to do dentistry without purpose. We evolved into defining ourselves as a private practice whose purpose was guiding patients to optimal health. We didn't have the vision properly in place and thus didn't live the mission as well as we could have. Team turnover plagued us. We got lost.

Our current mission statement is this:

> *To use our knowledge and abilities to enhance your oral health, comfort, function, and esthetics in a way that is consistent with your values, desires, and abilities.*
>
> *To earn your trust and hold you in the highest esteem when you honor us by asking for help.*
>
> *To use our influence to help you be as healthy as you can be.*
>
> *To be a force for health and wellness in our community.*

So how do you do it? Creating a mission statement is a great team exercise. A solid team whose members share your values and believe in your integrity and sense of purpose is invaluable in helping shape the vision and mission. These exercises also make it very easy for the team to embrace the mission with enthusiasm. That enthusiasm is critical to the success of the mission. I recommend that you set aside a handful of meetings over a few months exclusively for this purpose.

Assign one member to take notes for the meeting, preferably on a computer, and distribute the notes to everyone for review prior to the subsequent meeting. Begin with a few critical discussion points overviewing your vision of the practice. Remember, the right answers are the ones you and your team create. They are different than anyone else's. Here are the questions to ask:

1. What is our desired outcome for the people who come to us? If we are health-centered, how do we define a healthy person? If we have a different outlook on dentistry, what is our philosophy of care and how do we set a standard for knowing we've done a good job?

2. What roles do occlusion and TMD play in our preferred practice?

3. What is our involvement with sleep-disordered breathing?

4. How do we see the oral-systemic connection in our daily practice?

5. What are our goals for helping people control periodontal disease?

6. Describe the nature of our relationships with those who seek our care. Are there people who we will not want to treat?

7. Will our office have a presence in the community?

8. What procedures do we love to do? What are we good at?

9. What procedures, if any, do we *not* want to do? What will we refer?

10. Who is our target demographic and what do they value?

11. What role will insurance play in our practice philosophy?

12. What are our goals for monthly revenue?

13. What mix of services will get us there?

14. How will we attract new people to our office?

Obviously, these questions will stimulate a lot of thought, generate hours of discussion, and will most likely help you and your team see and understand things in a brand-new way. It will also create a very long and wordy document which you'll need to distill down to a succinct, easy-to-read-and-remember mission statement for all to see. You may refer to my mission statement as a guiding document and feel free to use any of the discussion points with your team, but please do not use the principles verbatim for yourself; it won't be authentic and you won't be able to live it.

Your vision and mission need to be based on your own uniqueness. If you try to be me (or anyone else), you will not be happy. Get your values on paper, write your own unique mission, focus on it intensely, and read it every single day. Make it part of your office culture. Or, as Rich Green of the Pankey Institute says, "Get it into your tissues." Love it. Live it. Enjoy it.

Craft Your Brand

Like it or not, we live in a world where people are led to believe that all dentists do the same thing: that is, fix teeth. In light of this trend that isn't going to go away any time soon, publicizing our brand or unique selling point is essential. If you don't get your message out there, no one will hear it. And when you are a professional who delivers health care, I have news for you: You are your brand.

Take your vision and mission statements and work with a marketing professional on creating your brand. Everything you and your team say, do, or write needs to reflect your brand.

How do people see you? There are people in everyone's life who cause others to cringe when they enter a room. There are others who cause people to gravitate toward them, anxious to see them smile and greet everyone. Which type of image would you like to cast in your community, your family, or your circle of friends?

Like you, I have lots of serious stuff going on in my life, but I refuse to let my challenges define me or diminish the pricelessness of my life and the people who grace it. Now, I don't advocate viewing life through artificially rose-colored lenses or running around with an insincere smile, singing that life is perfect to everyone you encounter. But our stresses do not need to be projected as misery to impose on everyone we run into. If we can realize that life is a good thing and that a smile and a kind word could go a very long way toward making someone else's stresses a bit more bearable, we can positively impact people wherever we go. We can be prepared to lend an empathic ear to anyone who would benefit from our listening and telling them: "I feel with you." And we can share and sincerely celebrate the good things in life with people. That simple attentiveness to how we walk through the world is a zero-cost effort in *branding*.

This simple approach can make you approachable, delightful, and good to be around, both inside and outside your office. It could also make you far more attractive as a dentist to people you encounter in your daily activities.

And, having been both the village gloom-sayer and the village empath, I can tell you that life is a whole lot more fun when people look and act genuinely happy to see you.

Here are a few easy tips:

- Smile and look people in the left eye. The left eye connects to the right side of the brain, which governs our emotions.

- Extend your body toward people when you greet them.

- Ask people how they're doing and listen quietly.

- Project only the positive in life to all but the closest people to you.

- If someone needs you to listen to them, listen non-judgmentally, generously (that is, without interrupting), and with concern and *not* pity.

- Dress neatly and respectably both inside and outside the office. You project an image all the time.

- The overriding rule: Let your problems challenge you but NEVER let them define you. You're alive. You can think, reflect, laugh, and love. Project gratitude for that.

Some Thoughts On Marketing

When I got my degree in 1981, advertising and marketing had just become legal for dentists. Back then, advertising dentists were considered renegades by their peers. Like it or not, those renegades were ahead of their times. Advertising and marketing are essential for most of us. I have done TV, live radio, newspaper, and all types of internet marketing. All of these things can work and are a ton of fun. They are also very expensive.

Please do not forget that the most effective form of marketing is word of mouth. It's inexpensive, highly credible, very personal, and easy to track and reward. Please do not hesitate to ask people who are happy with your service to tell their friends or write an online review. When doing this, try to avoid asking the person to do it for you; rather, ask them to do their friends a favor by sending them to you because *they* deserve the great care that you and your team provide. If you and your team believe in your hearts that you give great care, asking for referrals will become natural. And remember: *you* are what they are buying. If your practice is relationship-driven, you are the reason for people walking into your door. It's not your dentistry. It's not your incredible good looks. And it's not a coupon. It's not even just you. It's you, your team, and, of course, your brand. Get out into your community with your team and create events that reflect that brand.

If you're about total health and wellness, give lectures on oral systemic connection, sleep-disordered breathing, and more. If you're all about esthetics, put on a showcase of your work. You can also sponsor other like-minded practitioners in your community and invite people in both of your data bases. Cross-pollinating is a great way for you to get recognized by more people and to give a like-minded neighbor the same recognition. I have used hotel banquet rooms (expensive), my synagogue's social hall (not-so-expensive), and a non-profit's meeting room (a small donation gets it) to have events. If you provide a little food, market it together through your patient communication software and social media pages, and get a good topic, then people will come. Offer a prize for all attendees who sign in and agree to be put in your database.

Set Your Goals

Every self-help book tells of the importance of clear *written* goals. If you don't know where you're going, you'll never get there. Goals are your roadmap to success. The trick is to formulate them with good thinking, write them down, review them regularly, and modify them throughout the year. I like to break my goals down into four domains: professional, personal, financial, and health. I set goals for my practice, my speaking and coaching, my finances, and my health and fitness. You can choose any areas you want for your goals.

The important things are to give your goals some thought and to treat them as importantly as you'd treat your GPS on a road trip across the country.

Set SMART Goals

SMART is an acronym for specific, measurable, attainable, relevant, and time-bound. Let's take a cursory look at this and see if you can apply it to your life.

It is not enough to say that you'd like to earn more or to get more new patients next year. How much would you like your practice to generate? How much would you like to take home? Calculate your fixed costs. Estimate your variable costs. Determine your desired salary. Now you have your goal for practice gross and net (specific and measurable).

If your practice is generating $50,000 per month, is it realistic to expect it to generate $100,000 next month? You may want to get the practice to that level eventually, but doubling your gross revenues in one month may not be attainable. A good discussion with a management professional can help you determine a reasonable goal that you can hit. Setting an unrealistic goal can lead to (perceived) failure and discouragement. Parenthetically, if you fall short of a goal, it's *not* a failure; it *is* nothing more and nothing less than a learning experience.

It is very important that you approach your SMART goals with anticipation and not expectation. Expectations are merely opportunities for disappointment.

Anticipation is a far more positive way to approach your growth and development.

A goal of increased revenue certainly is relevant. Every business needs to grow. Adding six new team members next week is certainly specific, measurable, and attainable, but may not be relevant to your growth (it certainly may not be relevant to your increased personal income).

Finally, your specific, measurable, attainable, and relevant goals need to be time-bound. Set your anticipation of increased revenue for a reasonable-to-attain period of time. Good examples of this would be: "I will increase my monthly practice income from $50,000 to $55,000 in ninety days," or, "My personal income will rise from $100,000 to $125,000 by the end of the year."

Equipment Purchases

What equipment do you (really) need in order to accomplish your goals? Your vision is now taking shape. You're beginning to see your own unique *why*. You're hanging out and exchanging ideas with like-minded people with similar philosophies and you see that some of your peers have gadgets, services, and gizmos that will do digital miracles for you and you want each and every one of those expensive toys. Stop. Take a deep breath. Look at your budget and your cash flow and see what additional expense you can reasonably take on without causing any undue pressure.

If your office is profitable and there are extra dollars available to invest in the practice, choose your new toys carefully. Which of the latest technologies will enable you to up your game, attain your vision, enhance your people's experience, and increase your revenues? But be careful and consult your accountant before your major purchases. The last thing you want is to buy something that will force you to sell dentistry that is not in a person's best interest in order to pay the note for that cool new toy. Yes, people seeking your services like technology. But they like integrity even more and you don't need to add stress to your daily or monthly life.

One suggestion would be to identify a piece of equipment you want, write it down along with its purpose, how it would improve your practice, how you'd feel when you own it, and what it would cost. Put that number in a projected budget for your next fiscal year and see how it fits and/or how much you need to earn to pay that monthly note.

You can use the same process for every decision.

You and I are different. We each have our own perceptions of what constitutes a happy life. So, I do not have any tips for you on how to practice dentistry. What we will do is take a look at how *you* can create your own unique practice that fulfills your own unique needs and wants by using your own gifts and talents.

We can choose to be healers, tooth repairers, estheticians, providers for the disadvantaged, and myriad of other choices. In order to do anything fulfilling in dentistry and in life, we need to know ourselves first and foremost. Indeed, the beauty of our profession is that it offers us so many choices on how to practice.

Lesson 8

Align Your Physical Routine
With Your Goals

Our lives in dental school were peppered with constant critique of the flaws of our work. Some of the critiques were constructive and very important to our becoming professionals while others were potentially damaging to the way we see ourselves. If we are not careful, sharp criticism of ourselves can become a way of thinking in every aspect of our lives.

....

Understand The Following:

Your work is going to be imperfect 100 percent of the time.

Your practice is going to be imperfect 100 percent of the time.

Your finances will be imperfect 100 percent of the time.

Your health and fitness will be imperfect 100 percent of the time.

Your *whole life* will be imperfect 100 percent of the time.

....

So What?

My religious training taught me that we are made in the image of God, but that we are *not* God. Or, as Brené Brown says, "You are imperfect. You are enough." Please, please, please get that one thought in your system.

You have your vision. You have your mission. You have your team. You have your training. What is stopping you? Imperfection? A need to make it all perfect? *No.* My good friend and mentor, Mark LeBlanc, tells his disciples: "*Done* is better than *perfect*." You will always be a work in progress. Your business environment, your techniques, your likes and dislikes, and successes and learning experiences (some people use the word *failures*, which I consider another obscene off-limits word) will all change. Your action plans will also be revised many times throughout your career. If you've thought through and worked out a good mission, good supportive systems, and SMART goals, put them in place *now*. It's imperfect but it's quite good enough.

Good Enough Is Better Than Perfect

That is neither to say that we need to accept the imperfections in our lives nor that we need to ignore them and pretend that all is well. If we muster up the courage to see ourselves as we are, we can *gently and patiently* reality check our circumstances and make some changes to improve ourselves.

For our clinical imperfections, we can join study clubs with like-minded practitioners, choose mentors, participate in online chat groups, or take some good continuing education in areas we would like to improve.

For me, one of the most frightening experiences in continuing education were the *hands-on* courses, at which we had to actually do what the instructors taught us to do. I felt a fair degree of shame when I was not able to perform as well as others in various courses (seemingly) did. I came away from many of these experiences thinking I was inadequate.

Then, at the urging of a friend, I summoned the courage to join a Tucker Study Club. All of a sudden, I found myself in a large dental clinic with my dental assistant, a patient, and twelve of the finest practitioners in the state of New Jersey, along with an amazing mentor, Warren K. Johnson, DDS. Our goal was to prepare a tooth for a cast gold inlay with an ideally placed rubber dam, an ideal preparation, and then take a perfect impression, all under Johnson's step-by-step guidance. We also (gulp) had to photograph each completed step of our work for a post-clinical critique. One month later, we would deliver, finish, and polish our inlays to perfection, take our pictures, and sit for another critique.

We did this for eight months out of the year. The sense of stress, shame, and inadequacy I experienced anticipating seeing my work on a huge screen, in a room with that of some of the best dentists I know, was beyond description. When I realized that our esteemed mentor spent as much time critiquing the work of the more experienced practitioners in the room as he spent on mine, my sense of dread diminished but never totally disappeared. My study club colleagues actually patted me on the shoulder after critiques and consistently told me that I did a great job. Over time, I began to relax as I realized that I was improving. I was actually enjoying the process of seeing and improving my imperfections each month.

At the end of one session, I went up to Johnson and asked him about the significance of the flaws in my work and the consequence to the human being who was receiving an imperfect cast gold inlay he had just critiqued. (By the way, the creator of the technique was Richard Tucker, DDS.) Johnson put his hand on my shoulder, looked me in the eye with a coy grin, and said: "Alan, it means that your work will probably last forty-nine years instead of the fifty years that Dr. Tucker's work lasted."

Understand clearly that you will (appear to) be better than some dentists at some things. And some dentists will (appear to) be better than you at others.

That's reality (and perception). And it also has nothing to do with your adequacy or your ability to improve at anything you want. I am so grateful to Johnson and my colleagues for my Tucker experience, where I learned that all I needed to do was to become a bit better with each learning experience I had.

Choose an area in which you'd like to improve. Seek out the masters and study under them with like-minded others. Absorb their knowledge. Talk it through. Practice. And, while you're at it, make some friends!

Guard Your Health Jealously

Your body and mind are your most important assets. Do not take them for granted. Do not underestimate the demands that dentistry makes on both of them and, therefore, the need to practice healthy living as we endeavor to make others' lives healthy.

Like it or not, your health is critically dependent on the way you manage your body. As an ACE (American Council on Exercise) certified health and wellness coach, I recommend that everyone consult a nutritionist and engage a personal trainer for a customized wellness and fitness plan.

My good friends Kary and Uche Odiatu, DMD, in their book, *The Miracle of Health*, teach us that our muscles have no idea how old we are. They are so right. You can build muscle at any age. You do not have to get weak as your chronological age increases. You neither have to walk with a slouch nor have anything short of good muscle tone after three or more decades of dentistry. And you do not have to have chronic pain issues that we think come with an increase in years on this earth.

Here are a few *general* recommendations for you:

First, if you have not exercised in a long time or have *any* medical condition, please consult with your physician before beginning any exercise program.

Set a minimal goal of 150 minutes of cardiovascular exercise each week. You can walk, run, use a treadmill, elliptical machine, bicycle, a rower, or any device that gets you moving. You can go in fifteen-, thirty-, or sixty-minute intervals. You'll burn calories and invigorate yourself each time you do this.

Do you really think you don't have 150 minutes a week? Think again. Take a walk at lunch. Get up a few minutes earlier each day. Park your car a little further away from your office, the supermarket, the mall, etc. Walk around your local mall a bit. It is best to have a trainer (or a physical therapist if you have any injuries) customize an optimal program for you, but in the absence of any medical restrictions, *do something*! Start small and slow and build yourself up.

We are hunters and gatherers by nature. We are programmed to move. When our cells detect that we are moving, they get the message that we are living with a physical purpose and they respond accordingly. Moving was critical for our ancestors' survival and remains critical today. Our cells have not changed that much over the millennia.

Ideally, you want to get your heart rate to 80 percent of your maximal heart rate during aerobic exercise. This will need to be customized with a good trainer or, in the least, a fitness app.

Do not get discouraged if your progress to health isn't rapid because it won't be. Football teams score touchdowns a few yards at a time. The same holds true for fitness and health. Whether you seek weight loss, endurance, longevity, or just happiness from exercise, stay focused on what's in it for you. Most people who embark on a fitness program will experience a lapse in their motivation and/or participation. Assume this is going to happen to you and be prepared to ease your way back into your routine. Don't think of a lapse in motivation as a reason to give up. Do the opposite: be kind and gentle to yourself, give yourself permission to be imperfect, and pick up where you left off. At the time of this writing, I am struggling to regain my endurance as I have focused on my strength training while a strained Ileo-tibial band takes its time healing from overuse. I'm getting back there and I will not stop.

Understand, as well, that a prolonged disruption to your routine can cause a good deal of loss of its benefits. If it happens to you, you may need to go back to square one and work your way back to form. We see this typically after an illness. We also see it when a person just gives up and loses the gains they initially experienced with exercise. Please make every effort to put physical fitness in your routine. And if you're disrupted, be kind, patient, and gentle on yourself as you get back to fitness. Whether you're a great runner, a beginning walker, or anything in between, the point is to just be a little fitter tomorrow than today.

Do at least two resistance training sessions a week. Although supervision by a trainer is best, simple things like push-ups, planks, lunges, and squats will work just fine. If you cannot use a personal trainer, use an app or online resource to show you proper form and different variants of exercise to keep things from getting boring and to keep your muscles challenged. Understand, as well, that our core (our back and abdominal muscles), our balance, and our legs are critical to quality and quantity of life as we get older. Keep them very strong.

Joining a gym and engaging a trainer are ideal. But sometimes we need to start small and simple and there's nothing wrong with that. Push-ups are awesome. They engage many different muscles of the core and upper body. You can do them anywhere. Can't do a full push-up yet? Put your palms against a wall and push back. As you get stronger, move your feet further away from the wall. Work your way up to doing full push-ups on the floor, but be sure to maintain a straight back. Think you have no time? One trainer I saw recommended doing a few push-ups after each trip to the restroom (preferably not on the restroom floor).

Check out online apps for other exercises. Be sure to follow form very carefully.

Eat Right To Be Healthy

The stuff we put in our bodies will determine how healthy we will be. This idea seems to conflict very seriously with the tried-and-true principle that food is for celebration and enjoyment.

....

Let me suggest that it is not that difficult to strike that balance between the critical elements of our health and our happiness.

....

First, evaluate your physical condition. Get a thorough physical examination and look at your blood work. How's your HDL and

LDL? Your blood sugar? A1C? What are your risk factors and familial history for heart disease, diabetes, cancer, and Alzheimer's Disease? Next, take a look at your body composition. Scale weight is an OK measurement, but for the purposes of preparing your best nutrition, percent body fat (PBF) is a critical number to know. Men, my ACE training tells us that you're looking for a maximum PBF under 24 percent, which is considered average. Ideally, 14-17 percent body fat is considered fit. If you're an athlete, you can go even lower. Women, your PBF goals are a bit higher: from 25 to 31 percent is considered average; from 21-24 percent is considered fit. That is mainly because breasts are made of a good deal of fat. And the location of your excess fat does make a difference. Guys, that pants-button-popping, beer belly fat that we are prone to getting is dangerous. Android fat, as it is called, is associated with heart disease, diabetes, hormone imbalances, some cancers, and sleep apnea. On the other hand, large thighs and buttocks that women are more likely to have are relatively harmless.

If your body fat numbers are not what you think they should be, please do not worry and do not try to correct your problems quickly. No one becomes overweight in a day. The same is true about attaining health. Resolve to take care of yourself. See yourself as worthy of a good effort, learn to enjoy eating the right foods, and celebrate your success. A nutritionist can help you design a customized weight loss/fat-burning/muscle-building diet regimen. These lifestyle changes require discipline but they are both fun and worth the effort. Maintaining a healthy carbohydrate: protein: fat ratio takes a bit of thinking and preparation, but it's not difficult. If you need to lose weight, bear in mind that you need a 3,500-calorie deficit in order to lose one pound of weight.

As formidable as that may sound, if you can cut 250 calories a day and burn 250 extra calories a day in exercise, you can lose a pound a week. Add those numbers up over a few months and some significant changes can happen simply by some minor reductions in eating and a bit of daily walking. And if your need for weight loss is over thirty pounds, please do not worry. Set small attainable smart goals to lose your weight incrementally. Keep chipping away. If you have the wherewithal, work with a health coach or a nutritionist. When my weight, cholesterol, and blood sugar started creeping up to near-dangerous levels, I engaged a nutritionist. Eight months later, I was down twenty-five pounds, my blood work became excellent, and I lost another ten pounds over the next few years. My body fat percentage started at 32 percent and now hovers around 20 percent and I'm still striving to become even leaner. The great part of it all was that I was able to enjoy the foods I was eating, treat myself to some sinful delights twice a week, and enjoy my vacations with slight, *reversible* weight changes. You can do this . . . *Yes, you can.*

One more caution to you great people who may be morbidly obese. Your body type does not make you any less a terrific dentist or a person worthy of love and respect. It *does* put you at serious risk for illness and death and it can impede your ability to influence people to be healthy. Medical or surgical intervention may be necessary to help you. If that's the case, do it and do it now for your family, for those you serve, for your purpose on this planet, and for your enjoyment of life. Whatever your body type, please feel no shame and feel no comparison to anyone else. Be stronger and leaner tomorrow because you are worth it and you can do it. *Yes, you can.*

A Few More Thoughts On Eating Right

Since my transformation, I've become a missionary for healthy living inside and outside my office. I've studied and have become certified as a health coach and I'm glad to share my knowledge with you. Of course, I can neither create a customized eating plan for you nor can I account for any detected or undetected health issues that may be affecting you. Please consult your physician and, if possible, engage a nutritionist or a health coach before embarking on a program for good eating.

A few absolute, non-negotiables in my life:

I don't drink soda of any kind. Sugar and artificial sweeteners are associated with too many health risks. The pleasure of soda is simply not worth the potential cost to my health.

Fruit juices, even the best ones, are deceptively high in calories. Minimize your consumption of them. Drink water. Flavor your water if necessary with fruit extracts, readily available in health food stores.

Do not smoke anything. Your body is not meant to host a bonfire. Emerging data is showing that vaping is causing tremendous damage and illness. Don't do it!

Cut down on refined flour. Wheat was genetically modified decades ago to increase production as world demand increased. With that change came a change in the way our bodies metabolize it. Today's reality is that bread, pasta, beer, and anything made of wheat will make you fat if consumed in anything but minimal quantity. (*Wheat Belly*)

Keep your daily sodium intake under 1,500 mg. *(ACE)* This may not seem easy or fun at first, but the cardiovascular impact of excess sodium is profound. Watch your consumption of processed and canned foods. Restaurants add lots of salt to their menu items. Cold cuts, bread, pizza, and some salad dressings have lots of sodium. Pizza lovers, don't panic. Even modest reductions in your intake of sodium can have huge benefits. Bottom line: read your nutrition labels very carefully and cut down that sodium.

Trans fats are pure evil. They're found in margarine, many fried foods, commercially sold pastries, and processed foods. Please read nutrition labels and stay as far away from trans fats as you can.

Fruits and vegetables are essential. Work them into your diet every single day. Organic foods are preferred, especially in the "dirty dozen," as described by foodnews. org. They include, but are not limited to: apples, celery, cherries, tomatoes, cucumbers, grapes, hot peppers, peaches, potatoes, spinach, strawberries, collard, kale, summer squash, zucchini, and sweet bell peppers. Foodnews.org is one of many great resources to keep up to date with the impact of pesticides on what we eat.

Eating is a discipline. Food is fuel for your body. Good fuel=good engine. Bad fuel=disaster. You need to eat well 90 percent of the time. Allow yourself to indulge for two meals a week (not two days), because food is also a social medium and a source of pleasure.

Stay hydrated at all times. My nutritionist, Tom Bilella, DC, recommends that the number of ounces of water to drink daily should equal half the number of pounds you weigh. For example, a 160-pound person should drink eighty ounces of water. A recent statement in the Mayo Clinic's website suggested, to my utter delight, that coffee, *consumed in moderation*, can be counted toward your daily hydration. And I'm sorry to tell you that alcoholic beverages do not count.

Limit the amount of animal products you consume. And fiber up. Fiber, found in fruits, vegetables, and supplements, slows gastric emptying, increasing satiety, and causing you to eat a bit less. It also has a very essential laxative effect, helping to rid you of the waste products of digestion. For most adults, that means twenty-five to thrity grams of fiber daily.

Lesson 9

❧

Enjoy And Maintain Your New Life In Dentistry

S o you want to live a joyful, profitable life in dentistry? Here are some non-negotiable essentials: vacations, family time, and health maintenance.

Take Vacations. Vacations are crucial to your emotional well-being. I urge you to plan as much time as you can afford to get away from your daily routine. Ideally, two to four weeks should be devoted to recreation. There are many people who cannot take that much time away from the office, but you can take some time now. I cannot overemphasize the importance of this *and* the fact that if you don't have a large vacation budget, there are still plenty of things you can do. The point is to stop, reflect, enjoy, and rejuvenate a few times a year.

If you have a travel budget, stay within it as you pick up and get away. Whether you enjoy a beach, a city, or the mountains and lakes, just do it.

A week's vacation will clear your mind of your stresses, refresh you, and prevent burnout. If your budget is limited, stay home, take in your hometown theaters, restaurants, and sights. Just stay out of the office and ask someone you trust to cover for you.

And while we're on the subject of vacations, I learned early on to not have a specialist cover for me whenever possible. They cannot do all the things your patients may need to have done in your absence. Find a trusted practitioner of your specialty to help your patients; it's what's best for them. And, of course, be sure to reciprocate for your colleagues in need of a break.

Schedule Family Time. Time spent with your spouse, your children, your parents, nieces, nephews, and others is essential. There are so many things I wish I would have had time to say to my mother while she was alive. I wish, as well, that I had spent a bit more time with my son and daughter as they were growing up, helping a bit more with homework and creating more family outings. We did OK, but I personally could have done better.

Earning money and growing professionally are very important, but time with the family requires some strict discipline and exclusivity. Please block time in your personal calendar for date night, child time, elder relative time, and friend time. Although

I love what I do and I intend to contribute (read: work) as long as my mind and body are capable (because that's who I am), I will learn the lessons of my young dentist/parent years, and will always make time for my wife, my adult children, and, hopefully, grandchildren.

Maintain Your Health. Maintaining the physical, mental, and emotional health throughout your career is critical. Be prepared for times when things happen. You will gain a few pounds. Make adjustments to correct this as soon as you can. You'll get injured exercising. Allow time to recover, perhaps with a trainer, chiropractor, or physical therapist while you work the non-injured parts of your body. You will get bummed out during days or weeks when things are not perfect. Focus on what's going right and how much you've accomplished as you work your way through it, *as you always have and always will.* The stock market will cycle up and down. Let your financial advisor keep you rationally focused and don't fret. Sleep seven-and-one-half hours every night. And if you're crazy enough to fly red-eye flights across the country, prepare to recover from that for a few days by adjusting your sleep and workout schedules. On a personal note, every time I fly a red eye home, I swear I'll never do it again. As an imperfect and somewhat forgetful human being, I really have to remember my own words to myself.

When Do You Want To Retire?

The end game for all of us is that point of financial freedom when we no longer have to work. I'm not saying that you should stop working when you're financially free. I am saying that having enough money to live your life will offer you a level of freedom you've never known. Getting to and beyond this point requires some thinking and planning. Take a rational, unemotional look at your current financial situation with a trusted professional. Set a reasonable target date for financial freedom and craft a plan to get there. Follow the plan with strict, unwavering discipline. If you have to change your timeline as life changes, don't worry. And please do *not* use anyone else's retirement date, age, or objectives to guide you.

Barring catastrophic illness or some awful personal circumstance, there is no mandatory stop-work age. *Do not* listen to any pseudo-authority on what age is best to retire, what *you must* have, do, or think when you retire. The only authority on your retirement is you. Base your retirement goals on your life, your resources, and your desires. Maintain that rational plan to get your freedom and get excited with every retirement plan check you write because each one of those checks brings you closer to your version of a ton of fun.

In addition to Kenneth H. Cooper, MD (whom I met but do not know personally) who was working at age eighty-two, I know dentists and other professionals who have retired anywhere between fifty-five and eighty-plus. And one more thing about retirement: you may *have* to work past a certain point in life in order to maintain financial stability. So what? Follow the steps I outlined earlier.

....

See purpose in your life. Love as much as you can at work, at home, everywhere. Keep your body, mind, and emotions healthy.

....

You have tons of knowledge, lots of skills, and an ability to affect people's lives. Use it all with passion until your resources allow you some more freedom, and adjust your plans. It's about you and no one else.

OK, You're Retired. Now What?

Many of us dentists have been active, hard-working, competitive, and driven for most of our lives. According to the American Psychological Association (https: //www.apa.org/monitor/2014/01/retiring-minds), we dentists fit the profile of the person who has the toughest time with not working. The APA has also told us that that the initial euphoria of not having to go to work will deteriorate into unhappiness after a few years for most people. Please do not assume that you'll be happy sitting around doing nothing after an active life in dentistry or that you'll figure retirement out after you get there. We need to plan what we do *after* retirement as fastidiously as we plan what we do to get to that point. If you know your personal *why*, planning for retirement activities will be a bit easier. Regardless of your age or financial status, begin to look at your individual mission in life. Make sure it's in writing. Update it periodically. Do the same with a list of the things that make you happy and fulfilled. Talk it over with your spouse, your children, or your closest friends. You may even want to talk to a life coach about this critical element of retirement planning. If there's a vision in place that's based on your happiness, your transition from work to retirement will be easier and a lot happier.

I am driven to maintain my significance; that pursuit will drive me long past my clinical days. I am personally inspired by people like Cooper who, at age eighty-two, was practicing cardiology and maintaining a very strict fitness routine. My work makes me feel significant and I will maintain clinical practice and/or speaking, writing, and coaching while I enjoy my play time. I have friends who are living for their travel. Some have taken up art or music. Others have pursued volunteering or working in other areas. The important thing is to create a vision of retirement just like you created a vision of your practice. Live within whatever financial limitations you may have, but be sure to budget for or work for some activity that makes you engaged and happy. One word of caution on volunteering: do not do it out of a sense of obligation or in an area where you have no passion. Life is meant to be enjoyed. Retirement is life. Enjoy it.

Lesson 10

All The Things You Never
Learned In Dental School

I t's not news that the real world is much different than
academia and is changing rapidly. Academia neither adapts
nor teaches us how to adapt to changing conditions. Yes,
techniques change and improve, but dentistry is so much more
than technique. The pressures of a changing world and changing
perceptions of disease care and wellness care are forcing us to
choose a professional identity.

We use our knowledge to address people's needs, wants, and pain
points. The role of a healer goes way beyond teeth, occlusion,
and surgery. There is a critical human side to all this and it begins
with you.

Yes, you.

At the risk of a bit of redundancy, take a moment to look up from those teeth, soft tissues, TM joints, and implants and look at life around you. Put your work in perspective. Your dentistry is both a reflection and a fraction of who you are. Yes, what you do—as well as what you say and think—every day is important and it matters.

But let's not forget, as we dentists so often do, that there is more to life than what we do in the office.

Putting It All Together

To the best of our knowledge, we only have one shot at this precious thing called life. Live it in abundance, gratitude, and generosity.

There is plenty of work to do, plenty of people who need you, and plenty of niches to occupy in dentistry. Choose yours and go all in!

Practice Gratitude Daily. Every night when my head hits my pillow and each morning when I wake up, I think of at least three things I'm grateful for. I want you to do the same thing every day, without exception. Never, ever forget that the most troubled soul has things to be grateful for. So do you.

You are fortunate to have chosen dentistry as your life's work and to have succeeded in getting to where you are now.

Regardless of where you are in your career, what type of dentistry you do, or your personal philosophy of life and care, always remember that you are endowed with the ability to get paid for something special for people every minute of every day.

You are more educated and enlightened than most people who walk this earth and you have the opportunity to learn more every year. You are also imperfect, your work is imperfect, and you will certainly have disgruntled people in your professional (and personal) life. That's all OK as long as *you* are not one of those disgruntled people.

Understand that you are every bit as worthy as anyone else and that you are quite good enough as you are. Whether you're twenty-nine or ninety-two, keep growing and don't stagnate.

By this point, I hope you have found your *why*. I hope you've created a mission. You know who you are and your place in this world. Tell yourself over and over again who you are. Radiate that narrative in everything you say and do. I've heard people cynically say, "Fake it till you make it." But I see it differently. I would rephrase it as, "Define who you want to be, act the part with all your heart, take the steps you need to constantly improve yourself, and reap the reward of living your preferred life."

Goal Setting. It's all well and good to have concrete, tangible goals, but the most important element is *why* we want them. When we ponder *what* our goals will be, we need to give equal if not more thought to *why* we want them. What would it mean to you to have your income rise by 20 percent in the next twelve months?

How would it make you feel, by the way, is far more important than how you will spend or invest the extra dollars.

So, if you're creating a spreadsheet for your goals, create an extra column for *why* you want your goal and *how* it would make you feel.

Look at your goals daily and stay focused not only on the goal but also on the emotional benefit of your attainment. Let your heart and your brain work together. The results will be wonderful.

There Is Only One You

Stop comparing yourself to anyone except your past self. If you know who you are, why you're here, and what *you* need to improve, just do it. No one else's vision for dentistry and life— not even mine—should matter to you!

The Arbinger Institute's classic book, *Outward Mindset* (Berrett Koehler Publishers 2016) is another must-read for you. If we see our practices, our associates, our teams, and the people who seek our care as vehicles to earn a living, we are living with an inward mindset and will eventually burn out, suffer tremendous turnover, and experience no loyalty or support in doing our life's work. Conversely, when people around us see us as working for their well-being, we build trust, respect, and loyalty. This is the recipe for the success that comes with Outward Mindset. Are there things you can do for your hygienist, assistant, front desk person, or associate? What can you do tomorrow morning to make someone's—anyone's—life better? Get known as a giver and reap the tangible and intangible rewards.

Stay Humble

The importance of humility is worth repeating. We are every bit as dependent on people as they are on us. Listen carefully to your team. They see stuff that you can't. Listen to the people who come to you for care. They can provide critical input not only for their treatment plans, but also for improving your office. Always keep in mind that every human being we encounter is a story, just as you are. Everyone is struggling, celebrating, laughing, and crying.

What's going on in the lives of your team members? You don't need to know every intimate detail and you don't have to socialize with them. But it is important to show some interest in them as individuals. Remember that your success is as dependent on them as theirs is dependent on you. When your team lives in happy recognition of that reality, you've got yourselves something awesome and unstoppable.

Your dentistry is important, but it needs to fit another human being's life. What good is a beautiful *All on Four* to a person who's just been diagnosed with a serious illness or whose family is struggling? And if you don't mention that same All on Four to a person who drives a crummy car, you may be missing the chance to transform a life. Learn who that person in your chair is.

Listen to their desires and their abilities before you start playing with all your fancy instruments. Your dentistry and your life will be far more rewarding when you understand its place in another person's life.

A Few Words On Your Finances And Money Team

This book does not constitute personal advice, of course; it is all generalized. When it comes to your finances, that goes double. Your finances require customization *and an annual review* with a good financial planner.

Now, the general advice:

Please dedicate a percentage of your paycheck, from 3 to 20 percent, to a qualified retirement plan. Don't even look at that money; put it away and forget about it.

Make sure that your mortgage principal, interest, and taxes do not exceed 30 percent of your *after-tax* income. Live below your means and establish a liquidity account for your personal life and for your business.

Build an account that contains three to six months of survival expenses for you to use in an emergency at home and in the office. It's very hard for us dentists to live below our means, especially when we see the illusion of our peers driving big cars, taking high-end vacations, and (seemingly) spending tons of money which we may expect ourselves to spend. Falling into that trap may lead you down a very difficult path.

Enjoy life, by all means. Have some fun, for sure. But, keep your expenses real and don't look at anyone else's expenditures except your own.

Make sure you have enough disability insurance to pay your expenses and enough cash in the bank to cover your exclusion period; that is, if your disability policy excludes the first sixty days of a disability, have sixty-days worth of office and personal expenses in the bank.

Make sure you have enough life insurance to keep your family secure in the event that tragedy strikes. Some life insurance now comes with long-term care insurance attached to it. All I can say is I wish I had that option twenty-five or thirty years ago. Talk to your certified financial planner about that.

It would be very nice if you can put away money every month for your children's education. Even a little bit a month invested over eighteen years can become very significant. If accumulating the cash we're discussing looks formidable, chip away at it slowly.

Review all of your financial issues *annually, at a minimum.*

Most importantly, smile when you write all those checks as you invest in your and your family's preferred future.

A Word About Accountants

When searching for an accountant or any advisor you may hire, ask your like-minded friends and colleagues for recommendations. Interview a few of them. Trust your gut and make a decision.

A good accountant will help you understand your numbers, create personal and business budgets, and, of course, help you anticipate your tax liabilities. There are many accountants who devote their practices exclusively to dentists. For some individuals, these people can be especially useful for practitioners who are opening or purchasing practices. Make sure that you like him/her, and that he/she listens carefully and empathically to you while working in a very complex and potentially stressful subject.

A good accountant will give you ongoing guidance on your business's health and your potential tax liability each year. If your accountant is not giving you the information you want, ask them for it. Meet with the accountant on a regular basis to be sure that you both are aware of your personal and business realities. And if things are not going the way you want them to go, raise your concerns freely and openly. If they're not addressed, start looking again. It's better to make a change for the better than to stagnate in the unacceptable.

Don't Forget Financial Planners

You are a dentist. You have training. You are focused on your clinical, interpersonal, leadership, and management skills. You have a family. You have a life. With rare exception, you are not a money expert. Keeping current in dentistry is tough enough; keeping current in the ongoing, dynamic world of finance is challenging at best. For me, maintaining balance, sanity, and security in my life requires a trusted financial planner. For many years I used the wrong financial planning firm. They worked with many dentists who (I thought) were better off than I was and I blindly hired them. Their investment and debt management philosophies made me ill at ease; that is, they were not in line with my temperament. I thought their monthly fees were excessive (they were) for the amount of work they were doing for me (not much). They set goals that were unattainable for one in my position. But, despite my sense that something wasn't right, I stayed on with them, thinking that if the *big boys* used them, I would become a *big boy*, too. That was a huge mistake. Their advice, which may have been very good for many others, was not appropriate for one in my situation. The result? When my practice took a downturn and I became unable to do everything they asked me to do (including paying their huge monthly fees), my entire financial plan took a nosedive. Fortunately, I was able to find the right advisor who has guided me to financial recovery. Understand that the mistake I made in choosing the one planner was serious, but not catastrophic. My world did not come to an end because of my mistake; in all likelihood, neither will yours. However you choose to manage your finances, trust your gut, implement your well-thought-out plan, move toward your goals, and calmly keep an eye on things.

Bottom line: Look very carefully at financial advisors.

A good financial planner is independent, charges a fee for his services, and makes a living without commissions.

Make sure their philosophy on investment and risk tolerance matches yours and that they do not offer a one-size-fits-all approach for everyone. Most importantly, make sure that your prospective advisor listens to you carefully and fully, without cutting you off mid-sentence and thinking he/she knows all the answers to all your problems without hearing you out fully.

I am grateful to have been introduced to a fine certified financial planner who took the time to listen, empathize, teach, and gently guide my wife and me on a path to security and independence. He helped us clean up the damage done by our past errors, encouraged us actively as we slowly and patiently chipped away at our problems, and demonstrated a clear sense of joy as we progressed. As a result, writing that semi-monthly check to my retirement plan not only makes me smile; it gives me a sense of achievement as I work my way to financial freedom.

Getting Bankers On Your Team

Nobody likes debt. Loan payments are sources of stress for many people. However, there are times when financing things makes sense. Your accountant and certified financial planner will help you make decisions on when and when not to borrow. In the era of big banking, personalization is getting increasingly difficult. Keep your eyes open for local community banks and credit unions. They may have bankers who are more accommodating and flexible than larger institutions.

Four Big Financial Takeaways

Here are the four big financial takeaways I'd like to close this lesson with:

One. Doctor, you are not an expert on everything. Get over it and find a money expert if you need it.

Two. The right financial team for you is out there. A little research, some good questioning, and a bit of well-placed trust will take a huge burden off you.

Three. If you are a financial expert and have the time and temperament to manage your own retirement and investments, go for it. *However*, if your efforts yield results that do not meet your needs, there is no shame admitting it and finding help. It's OK to make mistakes and you *can* recover from most money mistakes with a bit of help and discipline.

Four. Maintain a relationship with a good banker. You never know what you will need on short notice.

And Finally

You are special. You are unique. You have talents that no one else has. You also have problems, weaknesses, and vulnerabilities. You, your work, and your life are flawed. But you, your work, and your life are very, very good.

> *Struggle is a part of everyone's career and life. What we do*
> *with these struggles determines the quality of the outcome.*

You've already read the story of my struggles, how I learned to embrace them and what I made of them. Let me tell you about one of my favorite success-from-struggle stories.

Lessons From Vinny Adinolfi

Vinny Adinolfi is a child of the Baby Boom generation who aspired to a career as a singer. Vinny had to "settle" at a young age for a career as a producer for a major record label. Vinny got to know, and produced hit records for people like Dion, Frankie Valli and the Four Seasons, Neil Diamond, and countless others. Vinny kept his dream of becoming a Las Vegas performer alive by sharpening his musical talent throughout his career. He played in wedding bands and other small venues. He also nurtured the natural musical talent in his two sons, Vinny Jr, and Nick. When the record company he was working for was sold, Vinny, a devoted husband and father of two, found himself out of a job and without a livelihood. Encouraged by his friend, actor Chazz Palminteri, Vinny took his family on the road to find his dream. For years, Vinny and his sons played in small clubs across America, often sleeping in their van as they traversed the country.

Luck has been defined as what happens when preparedness meets opportunity. In his fifties, Vinny got lucky. He was discovered quite by (what may be thought of as) accident by Las Vegas producers Alan and Kathi Glist. One conversation and a little bit of persistence led to The Bronx Wanderers landing a permanent show in Las Vegas. The group now features Vinny, Vin, Nick, and a few of the boys' high school classmates and has recently been named one of the top ten shows on the famous Las Vegas Strip. Vinny is now sixty years old and has the energy of someone half his age. The Bronx Wanderers perform six days a week, fifty-two weeks a year. If you get to Las Vegas, please see them. Their amazing music is only half the show. Vinny, in his seventh decade of life, carries both a youthful vibrancy and a palpable sense of gratitude and love for his fans that is infectious. My wife and I became instant fans of The Bronx Wanderers and have seen them numerous times in Las Vegas and when they come to our area.

The take-aways from Vinny's story are clear.

Embrace The Struggle

A successful man like Vinny had the bottom drop out from under him.

What did he do about it? He dug deep into his natural talents and his passion, rolled up his sleeves, took a risk, hit the road, and did what he had to do. The result? Magic! What challenges do you face right now? Are they financial? Technical? Emotional? If you know what you need to do, just do it. You know who you are. You know your strengths. You know where you need to improve. Resources are out there for you. How do you find them?

When The Student Is Ready, The Teacher Will Appear

The numerous friends Vinny made in the music business served as role models to get him ready to succeed. He did not give up, and his producers appeared, and the rest is history. Who were your role models in school and in your career? Was it an instructor? A lecturer? A management coach? Keep the lessons you learned from them in your head at all times. Are you now ready to launch your career and your life to new levels? Get those skills you learned from your dental rock stars off the shelf. Sharpen the saw, as Stephen Covey wrote in *The Seven Habits of Highly Successful People*. And very carefully look around you. Your mentor will appear, seemingly out of nowhere. Vinny's did. Mine did. Yours will, too. I guarantee it.

Fall In Love Again And Again

The Bronx Wanderers love what they do, over and over again, night after night, and it shows. There is no evidence of burnout in any of them. There's no sign that they're getting bored doing the same stuff repeatedly. In fact, every time my wife and I see them, we both appreciate the intangibles of their act that get better and better as time goes on. No matter how many procedures you've done in dentistry, maintain your love affair for the work you do and for the people you serve. Keep learning how to do things better. Understand what you're doing for people. Learn new ways to do things. Keep the passion alive!

Maintain Humility And Gratitude

The biggest thing that strikes me about Vinny is the gratitude he displays on and off stage. There is an unmistakable look of happiness and wonder in his eyes when he performs and when he and the band come out to meet and greet their fans after the show. During the show, Vinny acknowledges all the people who have made him what he is today and thanks his audience from the stage and face-to-face. The Bronx Wanderers do not leave until every fan who wants to say hi not only get to do so, but also get just a little bit of their hearts and souls and, of course, a photo op. We need our patients, our teams, our labs, our custodians, and our delivery people as much as Vinny needs his audience. How do you express that gratitude? Sometimes a look in your eyes, a warm smile, an evening post-op call, or a simple thank you go a long way to make your audience feel appreciated and want to come back. And as I am certain that The Bronx Wanderers feel the love of their audience each night more because of who they are than what they do, I am equally certain that you will feel the love of your patients as you give your love to them in your own way.

Pay It Forward

Vinny is the leader of the group. The young men of the band, I am sure, have learned gratitude and love from Vinny. They are as infected with gratitude and love for what they do and who they do it for as their dad is. You are the leader of your team. Infect your assistant, hygienist, and administrative team with the gratitude attitude. Let it emanate from everything you say and do.

No one person, book, or how-to course will contain every bit of information or knowledge you need to have a happy, successful, and prosperous career.

You are a beautiful composite of all the knowledge and experience you've encountered in life.

You are also the only one who can define and find your fulfillment. Your answers are inside of you. Use the knowledge you have, blend it in with your own uniqueness, and go find them.

Alongside my gratitude for taking the time to read about my journey and share the lessons I've learned is my heartfelt wish that you found something here to add to your wisdom. I hope that I have struck a chord within you and possibly inspired you to close your eyes, take a deep breath, celebrate the greatness inside of you, and become better, richer, and stronger. My other hope is that, when you realize the incredible value that your life holds and find your *why,* you will use your greatness to make others' lives a bit better every day you are here. Life is a journey. It has a beginning and it has an end. The road you take on that journey is bumpy. It has lots of potholes. And it's sometimes not even paved at all. There are lots of forks in the road, too, and there's no turning back. But if you fasten your seatbelts and ride down that road in a vehicle of gratitude with the heat off, the lights on, the windows down, and the music up, this imperfect journey and career you have can be profoundly rewarding and a whole lot of fun.

It's up to you. Enjoy the ride.

Appendix

─────〰〰─────

About the Author

Alan Stern, DDS is a practicing dentist, an ACE-certified health coach and behavior change specialist, and the founder and operator of Better, Richer, Stronger, LLC, a coaching service for dentists. His coaching helps dentists define and attain the practice of their dreams. His speaking shows dentists how to find clarity, purpose, prosperity, and happiness in the dental profession.

After struggling for the first thirty years of his career, he found prosperity by restructuring his practice around his own unique core value: happiness. As a result of his work with study clubs, conferences, and individuals, dentists rekindle their passion for the profession, earn more money with less stress, and live happier, healthier lives.

On a personal note, Stern has attained, at age sixty-six, a level of fitness he never dreamed possible. He holds a plank for ten-

and-a-half minutes and is training to reach even more fitness and health goals. At an age when many people slow down, he is better, richer, and stronger than ever.

Acknowledgments

I t is said that when the student is ready, the teacher will appear; over six-and-a-half decades, so many great people appeared in my life to change its course for the better. This work is the result of their presence and influence in my life, and I am honored to share that presence with you. At the risk of errors of omission and in the interest of brevity, I will mention as many as I can as succinctly as possible.

Long before I thought of my purpose in life, then through my critical, sensitive adolescence, pre-college, and college years, Wesley "Doc" Phelon taught me how to use my limited skills to become a very good ball player and how to influence young people in a highly structured yet fun program. I carry Doc's lessons in everything I do. Doc was my camp counselor, an amazing older male role model, a boss, and a friend. My give-it-your-all attitude began with the lessons Doc taught me. We lost Doc in 2016, but he lives inside of me and every person he taught, coached, and worked with.

Bob Ladenheim, DDS, the father of my very close friend, Marc, and my dentist growing up, gave me the direction to enter the profession he loved and the passion for those I care for.

The Pankey Institute taught me how to be much more than a tooth fixer and introduced me to some of the finest ladies and gentlemen who have graced the dental profession. Beginning with my study under Sandy Parrott, DDS, I learned that my work and my life have meaning way beyond my instruments and treatment rooms. In 1994, when I told Parrott how profoundly he changed my life, his response was: "Someday it will be your turn to do this for someone else." Here I am, Sandy.

I was fortunate enough to have engaged the late, great Arnold A. Lazarus, PhD, a world class psychologist, when I was pretty down on myself and my life. Lazarus taught me how to put things into perspective and see my life and career as wonderful things through Rational Emotive Therapy. How I wish he could see this book.

Peak performance coach Dana Ackley showed me how to apply those perspectives as well as Emotional Intelligence in a dental practice and in my life.

My dear friend and chiropractor, Raj Gupta, DC verbally beat me into submission at a time when I could barely walk due to a herniated disk and could barely see my toes due to my huge belly. Gupta put me through an extensive program that relieved my back pain without disrupting my career and introduced me to nutritionist Tom Bilella, DC, who, once and for all, broke me of my bad eating habits and showed me not only how to use food as fuel, but also to enjoy eating things that promote wellness.

The many trainers we have had, most notably Don "The Hebrew Hammer" Benjamin, who continues to teach us fitness and to challenge both my wife and me to go way beyond what we think are our limitations to be fit and powerful.

Financial planner James L DiNardo rescued me from near disaster and showed me the principles of patiently but surely and shamelessly working toward financial security and freedom. The financial realities I talk about in this book are from the lessons he and his team taught me.

Dental practice coach Marilee Sears popped into my life out of nowhere and has been my guardian angel. Sears taught me to believe in myself, find my purpose, and live it passionately every day of my life, in the office, in my speaking and coaching, and in my personal life. She has touched my soul in ways in which I hope to touch yours

Mary Osborne and Joan Unterschuetz are largely responsible for my growth as a leader, as a listener, and as a human being. I become a better person every time I'm in the presence of these two brilliant women. Any legacy I may leave in this world will carry the lessons they have helped me learn. If you have even the remotest chance of spending time with them, don't think about it; do it!

Roy Shelburne, DDS, one the most talented students in my dental school class, had his brilliant career and his life shattered, only to rise above it all and become hugely successful as a speaker and consultant. He lives the life of grace, humility, and resilience that inspires me.

Linda Miles and Lois Banta got me started on my speaking and coaching career. To have these two greats as role models and supporters is a privilege.

My business coach, the amazing Mark LeBlanc, continues to help me grow into the influencer, author, and speaker I want to be. Mark says that influencers never retire. I intend to prove him right.

Margy Schaller, whose knowledge of artful presentation has launched so many great speakers, has helped me become the speaker that I am today.

My publishers and editors, Henry DeVries and Denise Montgomery, have transformed my rambling thoughts on life and career into a coherent piece of work that reads shockingly well.

Finally, I am so blessed to have kept my college fraternity/sorority friends close to me for almost fifty years. Bob Stone, who we lost at age forty-six in 2002; his wife, Laurie; Mike and Judy Vernace; Alan and Clarice Wasserman; Tony Pantaleno and Michele Seitz; Barry and Denise Bass; and, of course, my college sweetheart/sorority-sister-turned-wife, Fran Copeland Stern, have kept me grounded and loved since I was not quite twenty-years-old.

To all of these people and so many more who have taught, inspired, grown, and loved me, I owe you all a debt of gratitude which I can never, ever fully repay. You have made me what I am today.

Works Referenced

Arbinger Institute. *Outward Mindset*. San Francisco: Berrett Koehler Publishers, 2016.

Brown, Brené. *The Power of Vulnerability*. Sounds True: 2012.

Crowley, Chris and Lodge, Henry. *Younger Next Year*. New York: Workman Publishing Company; Reprint edition, 2007.

Covey, Stephen. *The Seven Habits of Highly Successful People*. New York: Simon and Schuster, 2013.

Cuddy, Amy. *Presence*. New York: Little Brown Spark, 2018.

Goleman, Daniel. *Emotional Intelligence*. New York: Bantam; 10th Anniversary edition, 2005.

Harari, Owen. *Leadership Secrets of Colin Powell*, New York: McGraw-Hill Education, 2003.

Odiatu, Uche and Odiatu, Kary. *The Miracle of Health*. Hoboken: John Wiley and Sons, 2008.

Remen, Rachel. *My Grandfather's Blessings.* New York: G P Putnam's Sons, 2001.

Schein, Edgar. *Humble Inquiry.* San Francisco: Berrett-Koehler Publishers, 2013.

Made in the USA
Middletown, DE
17 May 2021

39033438R00090